UNIVERSITY
CAROL BOOK

UNIVERSITY CAROL BOOK

A Collection of Carols from
Many Lands, for
All Seasons

Edited by

ERIK ROUTLEY

EMI MUSIC PUBLISHING LTD.
138-140 Charing Cross Road,
London WC2H 0LD

First published 1961
Paperback edition 1978

ISBN 0 9505056 1 7

INTRODUCTION

The Christian Faith has been for nearly twenty centuries the light of the world. During that time its expressions in worship have suffered many changes, many perversions, many controversies; but also they have gathered to themselves many adornments, and the means of making the ineffable verities and the glorious mysteries friendly to ordinary men have been variously and ingeniously contrived. Not every such contrivance has proved of lasting or even of temporary value; but at its best the church's art, which has been the means by which the glories have been polarized through human imagination that the soul's sight might not be blinded by them, has been popular art in its simplest and most exalted form. The carol is now the most familiar form of this popular art of the Church, and it is towards the further-ance of the high pleasures that carol-singing can give that this collection is now offered.

It was not always so. The primitive church relied chiefly on the visual arts for the beautifying of devotion. The medieval church in the days of authority relied on the picture, the sculpture, the stained-glass window for the adorning of doctrine. It was only towards the end of the middle ages, when the ages of faith were already yielding to the ages of literacy and con-troversy, that the carol as we now know it was first heard.

But observe the strange ancestry of the carol.* A carol is, in its most ancient meaning, not a song but a dance, not a religious but a secular act. Fairly naturally, the word ' carol ' came to be used of the words that went with a dance-tune; but it was still a dance-tune. When men began to seek for ways by which music—at the time an art just breaking out of a long infancy into a troubled but exuberant adolescence—could adorn the church's worship, they asked whether the church's music must for ever be the tradi-tional linear plainsong which for a thousand years had alone been heard in its walls. Could this new counterpoint, this new free invention, be used to assist the church's worship, or must it for ever be kept for the secular singers, entertainers and theorists ? The answer, when it came, was the earliest kind of carol; and, paradoxically, it was a church carol, a fairly sophisticated piece of music designed for singing by trained singers in church. Its form was the dance-form—a refrain at the beginning and after every verse, with developing verses between its repetitions. The dance-measure—triple time with synco-pations—was preserved. But there was no question of dancing. Nos. 71-75 in our book are examples, freely arranged, of this form.

But what we really call ' carols ' now are popular ballads like ' God rest you merry ' (18). And the great characteristic which they all have in common is that they combine a sound expression of religious faith with an informal and innocent diction that makes them very suitable for singing elsewhere than in church. Experience proves it. Plenty of people sing carols—and sing them without a trace of self-conciousness—who avoid with some care any occasion for singing hymns.

* The reader may care to refer to my book, *The English Carol*, for a fuller account of these matters. E.R.

v

The English ballad carols, of which we have here a group in Nos. 17-29, cannot be dated with any certainty. It is useless to attempt more than saying that they originate somewhere in the general region of A.D. 1500. We cannot date them because we do not know who wrote them, and because almost all of them were written down for the first time in the early nineteenth century by a few enthusiasts who collected them from people in the countryside who could sing but (usually) not write. The words and tunes resided for anything up to ten generations—perhaps longer—in the corporate memory of a fast-dying agricultural English peasantry. Nobody knows whether what we sing are the original versions of tunes or of words. Sometimes parallel versions exist, sometimes a given set of words was sung to one tune here and another there.

But had it not been for Davies Gilbert, a London lawyer, and William Sandys, a Cornish gentleman, our carol-singing heritage might have been altogether lost. Gilbert published in 1822 *Some Ancient Christmas Carols with the tunes to which they were formerly sung in the West of England*, and Sandys in 1833, *Christmas Carols New and Old*, both after pursuing researches in the far South West of England. They were followed by William Chappell, William Husk, and E. F. Rimbault, and during the first half of the 19th century the printing of local carols gradually became fashionable, giving rise to such collections as *A Good Christmas Box*, which appeared in 1847, at Bilston near Wolverhampton and gave us several of our well-known carols in their first written form.

That classic document, the Preface to the *Oxford Book of Carols* insists that English puritanism was the cause for the decline in carol-singing during the later 17th century and that which follows. That statement can be put too simply. It was not so much the puritan way of life or the puritan religion as that urbanization, that elevation of commercial values which began to take place in those ages, and of which puritanism was only one (and a partly unintended) cause, that nearly killed the carol. The carol is of the country-side, and the countryside successively became in England a desert, and then a refuge for tired townees. Think of the history of Old Sarum: originally a village, then notorious as a ' rotten borough ' because nobody lived there, then later a place to which sightseers take a 'bus from the railway junction at Salisbury, and now in these latter days surrounded by arable land which is a field of applied science. That which is of the real ' Old Sarum '—and the carol can be so described—is likely to have a hard time under such catastrophic social changes.

But the ballads were rescued, and among them is some precious music and poetry. None is greater than ' Tomorrow shall be my dancing day ' (165); but even the selection we are able to give here shows what variety these nameless geniuses could achieve, what trenchant spontaneity in words, what strange urgent grace in music. It was a good wide vocabulary that could accommodate ' A virgin most pure ' (17), ' Awake, awake, ye drowsy souls ' (168) and ' I saw three ships ' (211).

Modern culture has, however, compensated any falling-off there may have been in carol-singing during the 18th century. We now have an enormous variety of carols, which broadly fall within the following groups: (1) Poems of early writers set to tunes which may or may not be of contemporary date and treated now as carols (e.g. 4, 42, 43, 46-48, 199); (2) Translations or adaptations of carols from continental sources: these are often very freely arranged, and not seldom are provided with new words. The whole section 102-145 falls into this category. (3) New carols whose words or music or both are written by modern composers within the last hundred years or so (e.g. many examples in Nos. 52-88).

The English use of foreign material is the special curiosity of our present century; but its inception we owe to that great scholar and translator, J. M. Neale. Neale came into possession in 1853 of a very rare and precious book of European hymns and carols entitled *Piae Cantiones* which had been published in Finland in 1582. He was so greatly taken with the tunes in it that he wrote at once a series of carols which were either translations of the Latin words associated with the tunes, or new compositions to carry the tunes. ' Good Christian men, rejoice ' (130) is a free translation of his, and ' Good King Wenceslas ' (215) a new composition, both written to carry tunes from that historic book, of which in this collection we have several.

The fashion thus set was thrust forward by G. R. Woodward (e.g. No. 31) in his collections of carols which led to the *Cowley* and *Cambridge* Carol books; Woodward spread his net wider, including music from German, Dutch, French and Italian sources, to which usually he wrote his own words. And it was at this point that the two figures appeared who have had the greatest influence in our present book—Edgar Pettman and Sir Richard Terry. It was these who first explored the astonishingly fertile field of Basque carols, and who enriched the English repertory with several carols that are now so well-known as ' The Infant King ' (121) and ' Gabriel's Message ' (5).

But here at once came a strange situation, for it was in 1928, while Pettman and Terry were doing their work, that there appeared *The Oxford Book of Carols*, edited by Percy Dearmer, Ralph Vaughan Williams and Martin Shaw.

Oxford stood at the end, and as the climax, of a goodly procession of compendious carol books. The first on this scale was Bramley & Stainer's *Christmas Carols New and Old* (1871), and that was followed by R. R. Chope's *Carols for Use in Church* (1892). *Oxford*, however, was a decisive book. It gathered up for the first time the results of that great period of folk-song research in which the great names are Cecil Sharp and Lucy Broadwood and whose results are printed in the *Journal of the Folk Dance and Song Society*. *Oxford* was a monument of careful scholarship, and a gesture against that vulgarization of the carol which was even then clearly to be seen coming, and which has now come. It set its face against the over-ecclesiastical style of which Bramley and Stainer provided a few and Chope very many examples. Martin Shaw and Vaughan Williams edited the harmonies, and some distinguished poets provided words where these were needed. A number of extended carols were included, and among these were some of the finest miniatures by the leading English composers of the day.

Meanwhile Terry was at work. He caused to be published a series of eleven pamphlets of carols, each classified by a style or a source, which were compendiously issued in 1933 as *Two Hundred Folk Carols* by Burns, Oates and Washbourne. The book is even now, only 27 years after its publication, something of a rarity.[1] It never had the success that *Oxford* had. But it was a

[1]Copyright in this collection is now owned by the publisher of the *University Carol Book*.

devoted piece of work, and Terry's arrangements of old music show a singular combination of faithfulness to the original with practicability in singing. This is to say nothing of Terry's own compositions—of which our No.10 is probably the best known. But between Terry and *Oxford*—for such things are ordained not only by divergences of taste but by the copyright customs of modern letters—there was an impassable wall: there is no Terry in *Oxford*.

Public opinion was surely right, of course. Of two books containing 200 carols each, if one had to choose between Terry and *Oxford*, it was *Oxford* that provided the greater variety and catholicity. More especially, it was *Oxford* that first made adequate provision for carol-singing at seasons other than that of Christmas. If other books (Terry included) made such provision, they failed either (as did Chope) in including only the most trivial material for those seasons, or (as did Terry) in insufficiently guiding the user of the book to the place where seasonal matter was presented.

This brings us to the present enterprise. For the last nearly forty years there have appeared in periodic succession a series of pamphlets, each containing eight pages and about six carols, entitled the *University Carol Book*. The publisher at first was A. W. Ridley, and Edgar Pettman had much to do with the earlier numbers. More recently the present publisher has taken over the series, and at the time of writing there are forty of these little volumes in print, containing 270 carols. Our present book is partly an ' omnibus ' edition of the best of the carols published in these books, and partly a new collection of material ancient and modern. Rather more than half of our 217 carols have been taken over direct from *UCB*. Of the rest a good number come from Terry's collection.

But what we have tried to achieve is, you might say, a synthesis between Chope and *Oxford*. Chope's was a church book—arranged by Christain seasons. *Oxford* was an anthology, arranged by sources and styles.

Our arrangement is one which we hope will ensure that the reader understands the importance of the words of carols as well as of their music. We provide a large central section of carols on the Nativity (17-163), and these are subdivided according to styles. This section thus displays an epitome, so far as we can make it complete, of carol-styles. You have here everything from ' A virgin most pure ' to a composition by John Ireland, and carols from sources ranging from Scandinavia to Spain. But round this central section we have sections whose titles reflect the major occasions of the Christian Year: Advent, Lent, Passiontide, Easter and Whitsun. Within these sections the carols are taken from almost all the sources represented in the Nativity section. An index is provided to help the reader find his way about the book in this sense. For example, if he wants to build up a programme of Basque carols, he can at once find that apart from the section 119-126 there are Basque carols at Nos. 5, 7, 187 and 207,

In order to make the book comprehensive and yet not too massive, we have (with the one exception of No. 85) confined ourselves to carols that can be written on one or two pages. This has meant omitting all ' anthem-like ' carols except such as cover only two pages; but of these there are now so many, and they are so readily accessible, that any choir will be ready to make its own selection and build up its own library.

But this book may well prove adaptable to all the chief occasions on which carols are sung, and we will therefore offer here a word or two on its practical use.

The book is for use inside or outside church. Our final section contains nineteen carols, all of which are of unusual interest, but most of which on the whole are best used outside the context of public worship. Some are founded on curious legends (208, 209); others refer to seemly but secular customs (199, 200); others again are of such general reference that they stand here better than in any one confining section—the last two are especially of this kind. But it is good to be able to include merry stuff like 213 and 214 in the hope that where carols are sung at home or in the church hall or anywhere else where outright hilarity is unembarrassed by sanctified inhibitions, these will get a hearing.

But one of the developments that has taken place since the publication of *Oxford*, and has considerably altered the reference of any carol book, is that of the Service of Lessons and Carols. This gracious custom, originated at Truro in 1880, carried on at Addington since 1883, and modified at King's, Cambridge since 1918, is now a national institution. It is used in some form in parish churches and Dissenting churches. And it is now beginning to develop as a form of worship for seasons other than that of the Nativity.

In compiling this book we have had this especially in mind—and perhaps more than anything else we have had in mind the development of Lent and Easter carol services. It is for that reason that we have separated out those carols which, though they speak of the Nativity of the Lord, speak also eloquently of our Redemption (164-179).

If the service of Lessons and carols is held on Christmas Eve (which is liturgically the right date for such a service) it should follow the King's College form as closely as possible. It is now possible to get, one way and another, its full text by referring for the Bidding Prayer to Briggs and Milner-White, *Daily Prayer*, or to J. M. Todd, *Prayers and Services for the Christian Year*. The Lessons are not quite invariable, but a reference to *The English Carol*—or indeed to the relevant number of the *Radio Times*—will furnish their references. It is usually a pity to tamper with this carefully thought-out liturgy, and to attempt to improve on the sacred felicity of Dean Milner-White's prayer.

But there is at least one context in which a carol service is now often held near, but not very near, Christmas: and that is in a school or university. Commonly the University term ends on Advent Sunday or the Sunday following, and carol services of this kind are held to celebrate the end of term. These should not be proleptic celebrations of the Nativity itself, but should be rather Advent services. King's College, Cambridge, has a dramatic Advent Procession, which perhaps can hardly be effectively held anywhere else. But we have provided an Advent section for the special attention of those who wish to hold early carol services. It is quite seemly for such a service to stress our Redemption, to attend to the story of Adam and to the Annunciation, to refer to the Nativity and to include at least one carol that looks farther, towards the Passion. No. 11, ' Gabriel's message,' is superbly appropriate—but then so is ' My dancing day ' (165).

Similarly a school or a college may desire a service at the end of the Lent term. In *The English Carol* there are detailed suggestions about the construction of such a service. Here again, if the service is being held, say, on the second or third Sunday of Lent, it is inappropriate to make direct reference to the Crucifixion in the readings: that should be kept for Holy Week. But it is quite proper to meditate on our Redemption, both on its conflict and its triumph. The Final Discourses in St. John, 13-16, delivered before the Crucifixion but dealing with promises of events to follow it, are ideally suitable for readings here.

Easter itself is a great day for carol singing, and the Easter story unfolds itself with the aid of carols and a hymn book without difficulty. Such a service at Whitsun should especially take note of the Ascension and of the Church's birth: carols of the Epiphany, showing how the infant Christ received gifts, can be associated with passages of Scripture recalling the gifts that after his Ascension he gave to men; and carols of the Christian virtues such as ' The Garden of Jesus ' (216) can be added to give depth and intimacy to the total message of such a service.

Of course, a carol can often be used for choral singing where an anthem would otherwise appear in a service. On the whole there is less danger of falling into malpractice through singing carols than there is through singing anthems; for anthems so often present a disastrous choice between what is difficult of execution and what is thoroughly complacent and vulgar. But the choral use of carols (even in Services of Lessons and carols) should really be always thought of as secondary to their congregational and domestic and popular use. They can be, and historically have been, adornments of the liturgy; but they are also the people's own Christian song, and it is in that direction that the modern carol, as we hope, will develop itself. The best carols are those which combine pure natural pleasure in singing with the salt of doctrine and good music. Good tunes decently harmonized, and words which with their traditional freedom and innocence can express the massive paradoxes of our faith: words which can allow us to ' rejoice in the Passion ' and abase ourselves before the Joy; these make good carols that anybody can sing.

We have included a few hymns. Some hymns are almost carols anyhow, and are wanted wherever carols are sung. We have included a minimum of these, because many more are in all the hymn books. But we have also included a few hymns which otherwise might not be known or regarded: 12 and 16, for example, 180, 193, and 198. In a service of carols the hymn book will normally be brought into use: but it would be perfectly possible to hold one (at Christmas anyhow) without going beyond the present book. We think that this adds to its usefulness and also (what is perhaps more important) gives it a certain balance and poise.

The *University Carol Book* pamphlets will continue to be published, and perhaps to lead the way in new developments of the carol. But we offer this book to Christian singers in the hope that it will provide simple but pleasurable decoration for their devotions.

It remains to thank those who have helped with its publication.

Apart from those whose copyrights are gratefully acknowledged separately, I wish especially to thank the Reverend T. C. Micklem, Mrs. Peter Scott and Miss Philippa Renwick who have written carols specially for this book (50, 92, 108, 117, 133, 139). And a very hearty word of thanks must go to

Mr. Gordon Hitchcock who, besides contributing many arrangements and compositions has borne the burden of seeing the book through the Press. Very little that we wanted has been excluded through copyright-obstruction, and we are grateful to all those who have generously co-operated in this matter.

And now, in Dean Milner-White's incomparable words—which usher in the singing of carols at King's College—

'The Lord Almighty bless us with his grace: Christ give us the joys of everlasting life: and unto the fellowship of the citizens above may the King of Angels bring us all.'

Edinburgh, 1961   E.R.

MUSIC ACKNOWLEDGEMENTS

The publishers desire to express their thanks to the following for the use of copyright material:

Composer or Arranger	Permission granted by	No.
Armstrong, Thomas	Sir Thomas Armstrong	118
Austin, Richard	Novello & Co. Ltd.	206
Broadwood, Lucy E.	Boosey & Hawkes Ltd.	171
Darke, Harold	The proprietors of Hymns A. & M. and The Rev. Dr. Lowther Clarke	198
Davies, Walford	W. Garrett Horder	14
Evans, David	Novello & Co. Ltd.	156
Holst, Gustav	The Trustees of the estate of Gustav Holst	61
	J. Curwen & Sons Ltd.	79
James, William G.	Chappell & Co. Ltd., from Five Australian Carols	100, 101
Kennedy-Scott, C.	Stainer & Bell Ltd.	86
Lang, C. S.	Royal School of Church Music	211
Leah, M. S.	M. S. Leah	68
Lunn, J. R.	S.P.C.K.	144
Mann, A. H.	Novello & Co. Ltd.	155
Nicholson, Sydney	Royal School of Church Music	205
Palmer, G. H.	S.P.C.K.	6
Sharp, Cecil	Miss Maud Karpeles, literary executor of Cecil Sharp	209
	Novello & Co. Ltd.	166
Shaw, Martin	J. Curwen & Sons Ltd.	88
Smith, Alexander Brent	Muriel Brent Smith	196
Stewart, H. C.	Executors H. C. Stewart	193
Terry, R. R.	J. Curwen & Sons Ltd.	10, 53, 54, 57, 77, 178
Whitehead, Alfred	J. Curwen & Sons Ltd.	153
Williams, R. Vaughan	Stainer & Bell Ltd.	22, 174
Wood, Charles	A. R. Mowbray & Co. Ltd., from The Cowley Carol Book	43, 105, 184
	S.P.C.K., from The Cambridge Carol Book	32, 33, 181, 217
	The Faith Press Ltd.	146
Woodward, G. R.	A. R. Mowbray & Co. Ltd.	131

WORDS ACKNOWLEDGEMENTS

The publishers desire to express their thanks to the following for the use of copyright words:

Author	Permission granted by	No.
Alington, C. A.	The Proprietors of Hymns A. & M. and The Rev. Dr. Lowther Clarke	195
Armstrong, Thomas	Thomas Armstrong	118, 140
Baring-Gould, Sabine	J. Curwen & Sons Ltd.	150
Bayly, A. F.	A. F. Bayly	68
Broadwood, Lucy	Boosey & Hawkes Ltd.	171
Burkitt, F. C.	S.P.C.K.	198
Chesterton, Frances	A. P. Watt & Son and the executors of Frances Chesterton	58
Chesterton, G. K.	A. P. Watt & Son Ltd.	59
Crum, J. M. C.	The Oxford University Press	186
Davies, John	John Davies	141
Draper, W. H.	J. Curwen & Sons Ltd.	190
England, Paul	Novello & Co. Ltd.	87
Epps, J.	Stainer & Bell Ltd.	86
Gallwey, Peter	Burns, Oates & Washbourne Ltd.	57
Heller, Ruth	Schmidt, Hall, McCreary Ltd., from " Christmas, Its Carols, Customs and Legends "	94, 99
Macbean, Lachlan	The Fifeshire Advertiser	91
Middleton, Edgar	The Frederick Harris Music Co. Ltd.	95
Milner-Barry, A. M.	St. Christopher's College	188
Offer, C. K.	Novello & Co. Ltd.	151
Ramsay, A. B.	A. B. Ramsay	66
Reed, E. M. G.	Evans Bros.	152
Religious of C.S.M.V.	A Religious of C.S.M.V.	3, 49
Sharp, Cecil	Miss Maud Karpeles, literary executor of Cecil Sharp	209
	Novello & Co. Ltd.	166
Studdert-Kennedy, G. A.	Hodder & Stoughton Ltd.	191
Wade-Gery, H. T.	Oxford University Press Ltd., from The Oxford Book of Carols	179
Wheeler, John	Chappell & Co. Ltd., from Five Australian Carols	100, 101
Whitehead, Alfred	J. Curwen & Sons Ltd.	153
Williams, R. Vaughan	Stainer & Bell Ltd.	174
Woodward, G. R.	The Faith Press Ltd.	146
	S.P.C.K.	6, 32, 33, 144, 181, 217
	Schott & Co. Ltd.	31, 135

Whilst every effort has been made to acknowledge owners of copyrights, if, for any reason, any omissions occur the publishers will be glad to rectify these omissions if they are informed.

All other copyright material is the property of the publishers to whom any application for reprinting should be made.

KEY TO INITIALS OF ARRANGERS
AND SOURCES

C.F.S.	C. F. Simkins
C.K.-S.	C. Kennedy-Scott
C.W.	Charles Wood (1866–1926)
D.E.	David Evans (1874–1948)
E.C.	*The English Carol* (1958)
E.P.	Edgar Pettman (1865–1943)
E.R.	Erik Routley (The Editor)
G.G.	Gordon Grimes
G.H.	Gordon Hitchcock
G.H.P.	G. H. Palmer
G. R. W.	G. R. Woodward (1848–1934)
J.S.	Sir John Stainer (1840–1901)
L.E.B.	Lucy E. Broadwood (d. 1929)
R.T.	Sir Richard Terry (1865–1938)
T.A.	Sir Thomas Armstrong
T.W.	Trevor Widdicombe
W.A.P.-C.	W. A. Pickard-Cambridge

Other arrangers of tunes:

J. S. Bach: 162, 163
J. Brahms: 137
J. R. Lunn: 144
M. Praetorius: 135, 136

CONTENTS

1. THE LORD AT FIRST DID ADAM MAKE

English Melody (West Country)
(E.R.)

1 The Lord at first did Adam make Out of the dust and clay, And
2 And then within the garden he commanded was to stay, And

in his nostrils breathèd life Ev'n as the Scriptures say.
unto him in commandment These words the Lord did say:

And then in Eden's Paradise He placèd him, to dwell, That
'The fruit which in the garden grows, To thee shall be for meat, Ex-

CHO. Now let good Christians all begin an holy life to live And

D.%. for Chorus

he within it should remain To dress and keep it well.
-cept the tree in the midst thereof, Of which thou shalt not eat.'

to rejoice and merry be for this is Christmas Eve.

3 'For in the day that thou shalt eat,
  Or do it them come nigh;
  For if that thou doth eat thereof
  Then surely thou shalt die.'
  But Adam he did take no heed
  Unto that only thing,
  But did transgress God's holy law,
  And so was wrapt in sin.
        CHORUS

4 Now mark the goodness of the Lord
  Which He for mankind bore,
  His mercy soon he did extend,
  Lost man for to restore;
  And then for to redeem our souls
  From death and hellish thrall,
  He said His own dear Son should be
  The Saviour of us all.
        CHORUS
        Traditional

1

2 ADAM AND HIS HELPMATE

Adam e sa coumpagno

Provençal Noel
(R.T.)

1 With-in___ a love-ly gar-den___ Dwelt___ A - dam long a-go,___ Ere sin___ his heart did hard-en___ And___ work his___ o-ver throw.___ His help-mate was be--side___ him, And there___ (till Sa-tan spied him) No___ joy___ was e'er de-nied___ him,___ And___naught he knew of___ woe.

2　To Adam's helpmate lovely
　　Did Satan whispering turn:
　'Come now, it doth behove thee
　　All godlike things to learn!'
　With eyes that shone and dancèd
　And eager hand advancèd
　She lent an ear entrancèd–
　Cupidity did burn.

3　Then, to her husband turning,
　　The Apple in her hand,
　She says in accents burning,
　'You too at my command
　Will eat this fruit before thee,
　And see unfold the glory,
　And feel the magic o'er thee–
　Will eat, and understand!'

4　Then Adam did her bidding,
　　And ate, and understood!
　His darkened soul o'er-riding
　　Came sorrow in a flood.
　From out the heavens proclaimèd
　A mighty voice exclaimèd
　'Go forth ye now, ashamèd!'
　'Twas God whose wrath pursued.

5　'Tis thus for him we suffer,
　　This day, by Satan bound!
　But Jesus came to proffer
　　His life to heal our wound.
　Our chains he strikes asunder,
　And free we rise in wonder,
　His love for us to ponder,
　In happiness profound.

Tr. K. W. Simpson

The words are translated from a Provençal carol in Saboly's *Recueil des Noëls*. The tune, which appears in many different parts of France, is here taken from Rouher in the version set to 'Nous voici dans la ville'.

3

3. TO ABRAM THUS TH' ALMIGHTY SPAKE

Nursery Rhyme tune, 'Philip'
(E.R.)

1 To A-bram_thus th' Al-migh-ty spake: From thee a na-tion_ life shall take__ and through this_folk_ the ho-ly__ Seed, all na-tions shall_ be__ blest_ in-deed: all na-tions shall be blest in-deed. 2 A Mai-den_sprung of Ab-ram's race To-

day hath borne the — Lord of grace; the — bless-ing — from the —

Bless-ed Springs, To all the na-tions peace Who brings; her —

then who — our sal - va-tion — bore, All na - tions bless — for —

ev - er - more, all na - tions bless for ev - er - more.

Words by a Religious of C. S. M. V.

4. THE HOLY SON OF GOD

So treiben wir

Wittenburg 1541
(E.R.)

1 The ho - ly Son of God most high For love of A - dam's lap - séd race, Quit the sweet plea- sures of the sky— To bring us to that hap - py place.

2 His robes of light he laid aside,
  Which did his majesty adorn,
And the frail state of mortals tried,
  In human flesh and figure born.

3 Whole choirs of angels loudly sing
  The mystery of his sacred birth,
And the blest news to shepherds bring,
  Filling their watchful souls with mirth.

4 The Son of God thus man became,
  That men the sons of God might be,
And by their second birth regain
  A likeness to his deity.

Henry More, 1613-87

The words are verses 1, 2, 4 and 5 of the 10 verses of No. 1 in Henry More's *Divine Hymns* (1668).
More, the Cambridge Platonist was a Fellow of Christ's College. His work had a profound influence
on John Wesley.
The tune is from a Wittenburg *Gesangbuch* of 1541 there set to a hymn beginning 'So treiben wir
den Winter aus'.

5. GABRIEL'S MESSAGE

Birjina gaztettobat zegoen

Basque Carol
(E. P.)

1. The an-gel Ga-bri-el from hea-ven came, His wings as drifted snow, his eyes as flame; "All hail," said he, "thou lowly maiden Ma - ry, Most high-ly fa-vour'd la - dy," Glo - - - ri - a!

* (Unison)

2. "For known a blessèd Mother thou shalt be,
   All generations laud and honour thee,
   Thy Son shall be Emmanuel, by seers foretold.
   Most highly favour'd lady,"
   Gloria!

3. Then gentle Mary meekly bowed her head,
   "To me be as it pleaseth God," she said,
   "My soul shall laud and magnify His Holy Name."
   Most highly favour'd lady,
   Gloria!

4. Of her, Emmanuel, the Christ, was born
   In Bethlehem, all on a Christmas morn,
   And Christian folk throughout the world will ever say—
   Most highly favour'd lady,
   Gloria!

S. Baring-Gould

* Optional.

Note: In the last phrase the passing-note B is often introduced on the third quaver-beat in the treble part after the double bar. This is a permissible variant.

6. THERE STOOD IN HEAVEN A LINDEN TREE

Es stot ein lind im himmelrich

German
(G.H.P.)

1 There stood in heav'n a lind - en tree; But, tho' 'twas

ho - ney la - - - den, All An - gels cried, 'No

bloom shall be Like that of one fair Maid - en'.

(C.W.)

Alternative harmony for two voices

3 'Hail Ma - ry!' qouth that An - gel mild, 'Of wo - man -

- kind the fair - est: The Vir - gin ay — shalt

thou be styled, A babe — al - though thou bear - est'.

2   Sped Gabriel on winged feet,
      And pass'd through bolted portals
      In Nazareth, a Maid to greet,
      Blest o'er all other mortals

3   'Hail Mary!' quod that Angel mild,
      'Of woman-kind the fairest:
      The Virgin ay shalt thou be styled,
      A babe although thou bearest'.

4   'How shall I bear a child, that ne'er
      With wedded man was mated?
      Pray tell me now this infant how
      Shall He be generated?'

5   'O Virgin sheen, it shall be seen,
      As I announce afore thee:
      The Holy Ghost, of virtue most,
      Shall cast his shadow o'er thee'.

6   'So be it!' God's hand-maiden cried,
      'According to thy telling.'
      Whereon the Angel smartly hied
      Up home-ward to his dwelling.

7   This tiding fill'd his mates with glee:
      'Twas pass'd from one to other,
      That 'twas Marie, and none but she,
      And God would call her Mother.

Tr. G. R. Woodward

The words and tune are from H. von Laufenberg's *Geistliche Lieder* (c.1430). The two-part version may be used for vv 3-6, sung by male voices in vv 3 and 5 and by female voices for vv 4 and 6.

7. WE SING OF DAVID'S DAUGHTER

Khanta zagun guziek

Old Basque Carol
(R.T.)

1 We sing of Da-vid's daugh-ter, Who bore us — Christ the King, — What time great Ga-briel taught — her How God from maid could — spring. The — news — of our — sal-va — tion O Mary how did'st — thou — hear? 'In

molto rall.

Ga-briel's sa-lu-ta — tion, All hea-ven — came down here.'

10

2   What did the Most High tell thee,
        How rang the angel's voice?
    'Hail full of grace O maiden,
        The Lord bids thee rejoice'.
            Where wast thou when thou heardest
                The angel Gabriel's word?
            'At home in Galilea,
                Alone before the Lord'.

3   When Gabriel so hailed thee,
        What other word spoke he?
    He said: 'Thou shalt conceive Him,
        God's Son thy Son shall be'.
            And were you troubled Mary
                When so the angel said?
            'Yea, was I troubled truly
                Concerning maidenhead'.

4   O then, what said the angel
        On seeing thee afraid?
    'The Holy Ghost will fill thee,
        The power most High o'ershade'.
            And did'st thou then believe Him?
                What answer did'st thou dree?
            'Behold the Lord's handmaiden,
                His will be done in me'.

                            Tr. J. O'Connor

11

8. ANGELUS AD VIRGINEM

Irish Medieval Carol
(E.R.)

1 Ga-briel to the Vir-gin came, And en-tered at ___ her dwell-ing, With his sal-u-ta-tion glad Her maid-en fears dis- -pel-ling "All hail, thou queen of maid-ens bright! The Lord of earth and hea-ven's height Thy ve-ry Son Shall soon be born in pure-ness, The Sa-viour of man-kind ___ Thou

art the gate_ of hea-ven, The sin-ners heal-er kind."

2 "How could I a mother be
   That am to man a stranger?
   How should I my strong resolve,
   My solemn vows endanger?"
   "The Spirit's power from on high
   Shall bring to pass this mystery.
       Then have no fear:
       Be of good cheer,
       Believing
   That still thy chastity
   In God's Almighty keeping
   Shall all unsullied be?"

3 Then to him the maid replied,
   With noble mien supernal,
   "Lo! the lowly handmaid I
   Of God the Lord eternal!
   With thee, bright messenger of heaven,
   By whom this wondrous news is given,
       I well agree
       And long to see
       Performèd
   Thy gracious prophecy.
   As God my Lord doth will it,
   So be it unto me!"

4 Hail! thou Mother of the Lord,
   Giver of gifts the rarest,
   Peace to angels and to men,
   When Christ the Lord thou barest!
   Do thou, we pray, entreat thy Son
   For us our long'd redemption
       Himself to win,
       And from our sin
       Release us;
   His succour too to give,
   That, when we hence are taken,
   We too in heaven may live.

Tr. by W. A. C. Pickard-Cambridge

The tune originally appeared in a Dublin Troper (music book for use at Mass) dated 1361. Its original rhythm is here modernised, somewhat in the manner in which Bach adapted the primitive Lutheran chorales, and the result is a melody of haunting dignity.

9. WHEN RIGHTEOUS JOSEPH WEDDED WAS

English traditional tune (Devonshire)
(R.T.)

1 When right-eous Jo-seph wed-ded was To Is-rael's He-brew maid,
   The An-gel Ga-briel came from Heav'n And to the Vir-gin said:
'Hail, bless-ed Ma-ry, full of grace,— The Lord re-main on thee; Thou shalt con-ceive and bear a Son, Our Sa-viour for to be,'

CHORUS

Then sing you all both great and small, No-well, no-well, no-well; We

may re-joice to hear the voice — Of the An - gel Ga - bri - el.

2 Then Joseph he to shun the shame,
   Thought her for to forsake,
   But then God's Angel in a dream
   His mind did undertake,
   'Fear not, just Joseph, this thy wife
   Is still a spotless maid;
   And not consent of sin', said he,
   'Against her can be laid.
            CHORUS

3 For she is pure, both maid and wife,
   And mother of God's own Heir;
   The Babe of Heav'n and blessed Lamb
   Of Israel's flock so fair.
   To save lost man from Satan's fold,
   Which Adam lost by thrall,
   When first in Eden Paradise
   Did forfeit by the fall'.
            CHORUS

4 Thus Mary and her husband kind
   Together did remain,
   Until the time of Jesu's birth,
   As Scriptures doth make plain.
   As mother, wife, and virtuous maid,
   Our Saviour sweet conceiv'd;
   And in due time to bring us Him,
   Of whom we were bereav'd.
            CHORUS

5 Sing praises all, both young and old,
   To Him that wrought such things;
   And all without the means of man,
   Sent us the King of kings;
   Who is of such a spirit bless'd,
   That with His might did quell,
   The world, the flesh, and by His death,
   Did conquer death and hell.
            CHORUS

                   Traditional

15

10. JOSEPH AND THE ANGEL

RICHARD TERRY

This is a version of part II of the 'Cherry Tree Carol', which will be found in full, with traditional tunes, at No 208.

16

11. GABRIEL'S MESSAGE DOES AWAY

Angelus Emittitur

Piae Cantiones, 1582 (R.T.)

1 Gab-riel's mes-sage does a-way, Sa-tan's curse and
2 He that comes des-pised shall reign; He that can-not
3 Weak-ness shall the strong con-found; By the hands, in

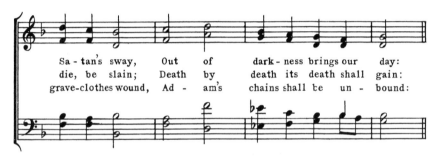

Sa-tan's sway, Out of dark-ness brings our day:
die, be slain; Death by death its death shall gain:
grave-clothes wound, Ad-am's chains shall be un-bound:

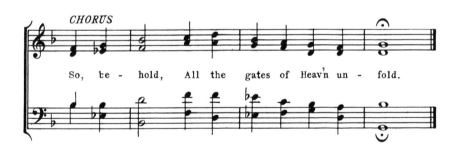

CHORUS

So, be-hold, All the gates of Heav'n un-fold.

4 By the sword that was his own,
By that sword, and that alone,
Shall Goliath be o'erthrown.

5 Art by art shall be assailed;
To the cross shall Life be nailed;
From the grave shall hope be hailed.

J. M. Neale

Suitable also for Eastertide.

17

12. CREATOR OF THE STARRY HEIGHT
Conditor alme siderum

Starry Height

MARGARET MacWILLIAM

In free rhythm: at speaking speed

1 Creator of the starry height,
Thy people's everlasting light,
Jesu, Redeemer of us all,
Hear thou thy servants when they call.

2 To thee the travail deep was known
That made the whole creation groan,
Till thou, Redeemer, shouldest free
Thine own in glorious liberty.

3 When earth was near its evening hour,
Thou didst, in love's redeeming power,
Like bridegroom from his chamber, come
From out a Virgin Mother's womb.

4 At thy great name, exalted now,
All knees in lowly homage bow;
All things in heaven and earth adore,
And own thee King for evermore.

5 To thee, O Holy One, we pray,
Our judge in that tremendous day,
Ward off, while yet we dwell below,
The weapons of our crafty foe.

6 To God the Father, God the Son,
And God the Spirit, Three in One,
Praise, honour, might, and glory be
From age to age eternally. Amen.

7th cent. Tr. J. M. Neale

The tune, here printed for the first time, was composed about 1925 for use at Fonthill School, East Grinstead, with these words. It may also be sung to 'The royal banners forward go'.

18

13. O COME, O COME IMMANUEL

Veni Immanuel

Thomas Helmore
(E.R.)

At Speaking speed

1 O come, O come, Immanuel,
   And ransom captive Israel,
   That mourns in lonely exile here
   Until the Son of God appear.
   Rejoice! rejoice! Immanuel
   Shall come to thee, O Israel.

2 O come, Thou Rod of Jesse, free
   Thine own from Satan's tyranny;
   From depths of hell thy people save,
   And give them victory o'er the grave.
   CHORUS

3 O come, Thou Dayspring, come and cheer
   Our spirits by Thine advent here;
   Disperse the gloomy clouds of night,
   And death's dark shadows put to flight.
   CHORUS

4 O come, O come, Thou Lord of might,
   Who to Thy tribes, on Sinai's height,
   In ancient Times didst give the law
   In cloud, and majesty, and awe.
   CHORUS

5 O come, Thou Key of David, come,
   And span wide our heavenly home;
   Make safe the way that leads on high,
   And close the path to misery.
   CHORUS

Latin, 18th cent.
Tr. by J. M. Neale

This tune is almost certainly founded on a plainsong melody; but in this form it is modern. The above arrangement may be sung in unison or in four parts; for unison verses any of the versions in current hymn books may, by transposition, be used alongside it.

19

14. O LITTLE TOWN OF BETHLEHEM

H. WALFORD DAVIES

1. O little town of Bethlehem
   How still we see thee lie!
   Above thy deep and dreamless sleep
   The silent stars go by.
   Yet in thy dark streets shineth
   The everlasting light;
   The hopes and fears of all the years
   Are met in thee to-night.

2. For Christ is born of Mary
   And, gathered all above
   While mortals sleep, and angels keep
   Their watch of wondering love;
   O morning stars, together
   Proclaim the holy birth.
   And praises sing to God the King
   And peace to men on earth.

3. How silently, how silently,
   The wondrous gift is given!
   So God imparts to human hearts
   The blessings of his heaven.
   No ear may hear his coming;
   But in this world of sin,
   Where meek souls will receive him,
   The dear Christ enters in.

4. O holy Child of Bethlehem,
   Descend to us, we pray;
   Cast out our sin, and enter in,
   Be born in us to-day.
   We hear the Christmas Angels
   The great glad tidings tell:
   O come to us, abide with us,
   Our Lord Emmanuel.

Bishop Phillips Brookes

15. O LITTLE TOWN OF BETHLEHEM
(2nd tune)

Forest Green

English traditional melody
(T.W.)

16. LIFT UP YOUR HEADS

J. A. FREYLINGHAUSEN
(E.R.)

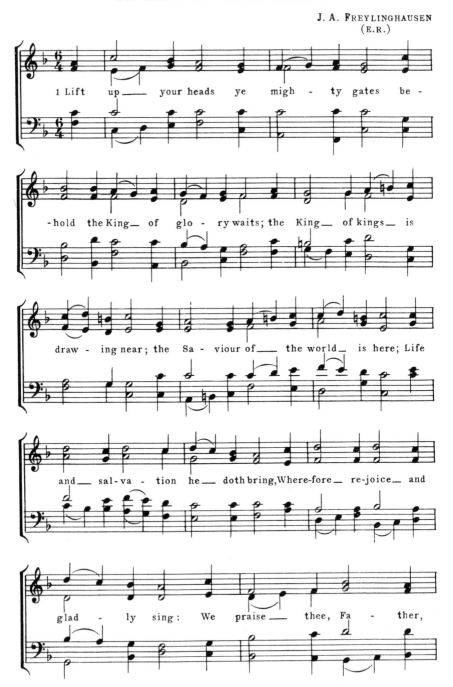

1 Lift up__ your heads ye migh - ty gates be -hold the King__ of glo - ry waits; the King__ of kings__ is draw - ing near; the Sa - viour of__ the world__ is here; Life and__ sal-va - tion he__ doth bring, Where-fore__ re-joice__ and glad - ly sing: We praise__ thee, Fa - ther,

now: Cre - a - tor wise___ art Thou!___

2   The Lord is just, a Helper tried,
    With mercy ever at His side;
    His kingly crown is holiness,
    His sceptre, pity in distress,
    The end of all our woe He brings,
    Wherefore the earth is glad and sings:
      We praise thee, Saviour, now
      Mighty in deed art Thou!

3   O blest the land, the city blest
    Where Christ the Ruler is confessed;
    O happy hearts and happy homes
    To whom this King in triumph comes;
    The cloudless sun of joy He is,
    Who bringeth pure delight and bliss:
      O Comforter Divine,
      What boundless grace is Thine!

G. Weissel, 1590 - 1635
Tr. Catherine Winkworth.

This great Advent hymn, by Georg Weissel, burgomaster of Domnau, was first published (in 5 verses) in *Preussiche Fest Lieder* (1642). The tune, which was composed by J. A. Freylinghausen in 1704, has since then always been regarded as the 'proper' tune for these words.

B*

17. A VIRGIN MOST PURE

English traditional
(T.W.)

1. A vir - gin most pure, as the pro - phets do tell, Hath brought forth a ba - by, as it hath be - fel, To be our Re - deem - er from death, hell, and sin, Which A - dam's trans - gres - sion hath wrap-pèd us in.

CHORUS

f Aye and there - fore be mer - ry, re - joice and be you

mer - ry, Set sor - rows a - side;_____ Christ

Je - sus our Sa - viour was born on this tide.

2. At Bethlem in Jewry a city there was,
   Where Joseph and Mary together did pass,
   And there to be taxèd with many one mo',
   For Caesar commanded the same should be so:

3. But when they had entered the city so fair,
   A number of people so mighty was there,
   That Joseph and Mary, whose substance was small,
   Could find in the inn there no lodging at all:

4. Then were they constrained in a stable to lie,
   Where horses and asses they used for to tie;
   Their lodging so simple they took it no scorn:
   But against the next morning our Saviour was born:

5. The King of all kings to this world being brought,
   Small store of fine linen to wrap him was sought;
   And when she had swaddled her young son so sweet,
   Within an ox-manger she laid him to sleep:

6. Then God sent an angel from Heaven so high,
   To certain poor shepherds in fields where they lie,
   And bade them no longer in sorrow to stay,
   Because that our Saviour was born on this day:

7. Then presently after the shepherds did spy
   A number of angels that stood in the sky;
   Then joyfully talkèd, and sweetly did sing,
   To God be all glory, our heavenly King:

English traditional

Words and tune from Gilbert. A corrupt (but still pleasant) form of the tune, inaccurately
noted by Sandys, was printed in Bramley and Stainer. See *E.C.*

18. GOD REST YOU MERRY, GENTLEMEN

English Carol tune
Harmonized chiefly by John Stainer

3   From God, our heavenly Father,
      A blessèd angel came,
    And unto certain shepherds
      Brought tidings of the same,
    That there was born in Bethlehem
      The Son of God by name.
        O tidings of comfort and joy!

4   'Fear not' then said the angel,
      'Let nothing you affright,
    This day is born a Saviour
      Of a pure Virgin bright;
    So frequently to vanquish all
      The friends of Satan quite'.
        O tidings of comfort and joy!

5   The shepherds at these tidings,
      Rejoicèd much in mind,
    And left their flocks a-feeding
      In tempest, storm, and wind,
    And went to Bethlehem straightway
      This Blessed Babe to find.
        O tidings of comfort and joy!

6   But when they came to Bethlehem
      Where our dear Saviour lay,
    They found Him in a manger,
      Where oxen feed on hay;
    His mother, Mary, kneeling,
      Unto the Lord did pray.
        O tidings of comfort and joy!

7   Now to the Lord sing praises,
      All you within the place,
    And with true love and brotherhood
      Each other now embrace;
    This holy tide of Christmas
      All other doth deface.
        O tidings of comfort and joy!

Traditional

19. A CHILD THIS DAY IS BORN

Traditional

1. A Child this day is ___ born, A
Refrain No - well, No - well, No - well, No -

2. These ti - dings shep - herds heard Whilst
3. Then was there with the ___ An - gel An

1. Child of high re - nown; Most wor - thy of ___ a
- well sing all ___ we may, Be - cause the King of

2. watch - ing o'er their fold; 'Twas by an An - gel
3. host in - con - tin - ent Of heav - en - ly bright

Repeat for Refrain

1. scep - tre, A scep - tre and a crown.
all ___ Kings Was born on Christ - mas day.

2. un - to them That night re - vealed and told.
3. sold - iers, All from the high - est sent.

4. They praised the Lord our God,
And our celestial King:
All glory be in Paradise,
This heavenly host do sing.

5. All glory be to God,
That sitteth still on high,
With praises and with triumph great,
And joyful melody.

Traditional

Words and tune from Sandys.

28

20. THIS ENDRIS NIGHT

Medieval Carol
(C. F. S.)

1. This end - ris night I saw a sight, A
4. That child or man that will or can Be

star as bright as day, and ev - er a - mong a
mer - ry up - on my day To bliss him bring, and

maid - en sang; "By - by, lu - lay lul - lay."
I shall sing, "Lul - lay, lul - lay, lul - lay."

TENOR SOLO*

2. This Vir - gin clear with - out en fear, Un - to her Son gan say, "My
3. Now my sweet Son, Since it is so, All things are at thy Will, Grant

Son, my Lord, my Fa - ther dere, Why li - est Thou in hay?
me I pray this boon to - day if it be right and **skill.

★ Solo optional—all verses S.A.T.B. if desired.
★★ skill = fitting
Words and tune, 15th century English.

29

21. TO-DAY OUR GOD OF HIS GREAT MERCIE

Kent Carol
(E. P.)

1. To - day our God of His great mer - cie Hath sent His Son with us to be, To dwell with us in ve - ri - ty, God who is our Sa - viour, God who is our Sa - viour.

2. To-day in Bethlehem did befall,
   A child was born in ox's stall,
   Who needs must die to save us all,
   God, who is, etc.

Trebles or Solo voice

3. To-day there spake an angel bright,
   To shepherds there who watched by night,
   And bade them take their way forthright
   To God, who is, etc.

4. Therefore 'tis meet we kneel to-day,
   And Christ, who died on cross, we pray
   To show His Grace to us alway,
   God, who is, etc.

English 15th century carol.

★ To be sung as two crotchets in verse 3.

22. ON CHRISTMAS NIGHT

Sussex Carol collected by
R. VAUGHAN WILLIAMS
(R.T.)

1. On Christ-mas night all Chris-tians sing, To hear the news the an-gels bring On Christ-mas night all Chris-tians sing, To hear the news the an-gels bring. News of great joy, news of great mirth, News of our mer-ci-ful King's birth.

2. When sin departs before Thy grace
Then life and health come in its place.
When sin departs before Thy grace
Then life and health come in its place.
Angels and men with joy may sing,
All for to see the new-born King.

3. All out of darkness we have light,
Which made the angels sing this night;
All out of darkness we have light,
Which made the angels sing this night;
"Glory to God, and peace to men
Now and for evermore. Amen."

Traditional

Words from 'A Good Christmas Box' (1842)
The first two couplets of each verse should if possible be sung antiphonally.

31

23. LET ALL THAT ARE TO MIRTH INCLINED

West Country Carol
(R.T.)

1. Let all that are to mirth in-clined, Con-sid-er well and bear in mind, What our good God for us has done, In send-ing his be-lov-èd Son.

CHORUS

For to re - deem our souls from thrall, Christ is the Sa - viour of us all.

2. Let all your songs and praises be,
   Unto His Heavenly Majesty;
   And evermore; amongst our mirth.
   Remember Christ our Saviour's birth.
   CHORUS

3. Near Bethlehem some Shepherds keep
   Their flocks and herds of feeding sheep;
   To whom God's Angel did appear,
   Which put the shepherds in great fear.
   CHORUS

4. 'Prepare and go,' the Angel said,
   'To Bethlehem, be not afraid;
   There shall you find this blessed morn,
   The princely Babe, sweet Jesus born.'
   CHORUS

5. With thankful heart and joyful mind,
   The Shepherds went this Babe to find,
   And as the Heav'nly Angels told,
   They did our Saviour Christ behold.
   CHORUS

6. Within a manger was He laid,
   The Virgin Mary by Him staid;
   Attending on the Lord of life,
   Being both mother, maid, and wife.
   CHORUS

7. Three Eastern Wise Men from afar,
   Directed by a glorious star;
   Came boldly on, and made no stay,
   Until they came where Jesus lay.
   CHORUS

8. And being come unto the place
   Where the blessed Messiah was,
   They humbly laid before His feet
   Their gifts of gold and odours sweet.
   CHORUS

9. See how the Lord of Heaven and earth,
   Shewed himself lowly in His birth;
   A sweet example for mankind,
   To learn and bear an humble mind.
   CHORUS

10. No costly robes nor rich attire,
    Did Jesus Christ our Lord desire;
    No music nor sweet harmony,
    Till glorious music from on high.
    CHORUS

11. Did in melodious manner sing,
    Praises unto our Heav'nly King;
    All honour, glory, might, and pow'r,
    Be unto Christ our Sa-vi-our.
    CHORUS

12. If quires of Angels did rejoice,
    Well may Mankind with heart and voice,
    Sing praises to the God of Heav'n,
    That unto us His Son has given.
    CHORUS

Traditional

Words and melody from Gilbert.

33

24. REJOICE AND BE MERRY

English traditional

English traditional
(R.T.)

1 Re - joice and be mer - ry in songs and in mirth! O
2 A hea - ven - ly vi - sion ap - peared in the sky! Vast
3 Like - wise a bright star in the sky did ap - pear, Which
4 And when they were come, they their trea - sures un - fold, And

praise our Re - deem - er, ___ all mor - tals on earth! For
num - bers of an - gels ___ the Shep - herds did spy, *cresc.* Pro -
led the Wise Men from ___ the east to draw near; *cresc.* They
un - to him off - ered ___ myrrh, in - cense, and gold. *cresc.* So

this is the birth - day of Je - sus our ___ King,
claim - ing the birth - day of Je - sus our ___ King,
found the Mes - si - ah, sweet Je - sus our ___ King,   Who
bless - èd for ev - er be Je - sus our ___ King,

brought us sal - va - tion— his praise - es we'll sing!

Words and tune from Dorset

25. THE GOLDEN CAROL
of the Three Kings

1. We saw a light shine out a-far, On Christmas in the morn-ing, And
2. Oh! ev-er thought be of his name, On Christmas in the morn-ing, Who

straight we knew Christ's star it was, Bright beaming in the morn-ing. Then
bore for us both grief and shame, Af-flic-tion's sharpest scorn-ing. And

did we fall on bend-ed knee, On Christmas in the morn-ing, And
may we die (when death shall come,) On Christmas in the morn-ing, And

prais'd the Lord, who'd let us see, His glo-ry at its dawn-ing.
see in heav'n, our glor-ious home, The star of Christmas morn-ing.

26. THE FIRST NOWELL

English traditional
(J.S.)

f 1. The first Nowell the angel did say, Was to certain poor shepherds in fields as they lay; In fields where they lay keeping their sheep, On a cold winter's night that was so deep.

REFRAIN (Full)

f No - well,— No - well, No - well,— No - well,—

Born is the King — of Is - ra - el.

Boys (unis.)   2. They lookèd up and saw a star,
Shining in the east, beyond them far,
And to the earth it gave great light,
And so it continued both day and night.
Nowell, etc.

Men (unis.)   3. And by the light of that same star,
Three wisemen came from country far;
To seek for a King was their intent,
And to follow the star wherever it went.
Nowell, etc.

Full harmony
or Quartet   4. This star drew nigh unto the north-west,
O'er Bethlehem it took its rest,
And there it did both stop and stay,
Right over the place where Jesus lay.
Nowell, etc.

Full harmony   5. Then entered in those wisemen three,
Full reverently upon their knee,
And offered there, in his presence,
Their gold, and myrrh, and frankincense.
Nowell, etc.

Full (unis.)   6. Then let us all with one accord,
Sing praises to our heavenly Lord,
That hath made heaven and earth of nought,
And with His blood mankind hath bought.
Nowell, etc.

Traditional

27. THE JOYFUL SOUNDS OF SALVATION

English Traditional melody
(R. T.)

1. In the reign of great Caes - ar, the Em-per-or of
2. Great Caes - ar com - mand - ed and or - dered it

Rome, The work of sal - va - tion for
so, The world should be tax - ed, the

sin - ners was done By Hea - ven's de -
high and the low; Each one to his

- cree for a___ Babe it___ was sent, ___ A
ci - ty this___ tax went to pay, ___ So

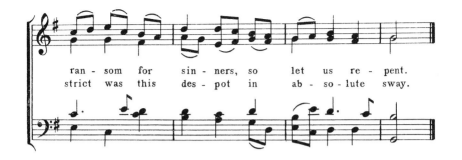

ran - som   for   sin - ners,   so   let   us   re - pent.
strict   was   this   des - pot   in   ab - so - lute   sway.

3. From Nazareth and Bethlehem in Jewry it was,
   That Joseph and Mary together did pass;
   These two to be taxed with the others did go,
   For Caesar commanded and ordered it so.

4. They both having entered the city so fair,
   Such numbers of people so mighty were there,
   That Joseph and Mary, their substance being small,
   Could get at the inns no lodging at all.

5. So they were constrained in a stable to lie,
   Where oxen and asses they used to tie;
   Although mean their lodging they thought it no scorn;
   And early next morning our Saviour was born.

6. Then God sent an Angel from heaven so high
   To certain poor shepherds in fields that did lie,
   And bade them no longer in sorrow to stay,
   For their blessèd Saviour was born on that day.

7. And presently after the shepherds did spy
   A great host of Angels appeared in the sky,
   Who merrily talked, and sweetly did sing;
   All glory to God and their heavenly King.

Traditional

Words from Husk's *Songs of the Nativity* (1855)

28. CHRIST IS BORN OF MAIDEN FAIR

Surrey Carol
(G.H.)

1 Christ is born of maid - en fair; ____
2 Shep - herds saw those an - gels bright ____
3 Christ is come to save man - kind, ____

Hark the her - alds in the air, Thus a - dor - ing
Car - ol - ling in glo - rious light: God, His Son, is
As in Ho - ly Page we find; There - fore bear this

des - cant there: ⎫
born to - night! ⎬ "In Ex - cel - sis Glo - ri - a"
song in mind: ⎭

This carol was collected by Alice Gillington who noted down many carols from gypsies in Surrey and elsewhere. The carol appeared in "Old Christmas Carols of the Southern Counties" now out of print. Some of the harmony has been borrowed from Alice Gillington's own setting. G.H.
*Or in E♭

29. THE OLD YEAR

Greensleeves

16th century English song
(E.R.)

1 The Old Year now a-way is fled the New Year it_ is en-ter-ed, Then
2 The name-day now of Christ we keep who for our sins did of-ten weep, His

3 And now with New Year's gifts each friend un-to each o-ther they do send: God

let_ us now our sins down-tread and joy-ful-ly all_ ap-pear:
hands and feet were woun-ded deep and his bles-sed side with a spear:

grant we may all our lives a-mend and that the truth may ap-pear._

Let's mer-ry be this day, and let us now with sport and play
His head they crown'd with thorn, and at him they did laugh and scorn

Now like the snake, your skin cast off, of e-vil thoughts and sin

Hang grief, cast care a-way;_ God send you a hap-py New Year!
Who for_ our good was born; God send you a hap-py New Year!

And so the year be-gin; God send you a hap-py New Year.

The words are taken from *New Christmas Carols* (1642) in the collection of Antony à Wood, in the Bodleian Library, Oxford.

41

30. OH, WHO WOULD BE A SHEPHERD BOY?

Traditional dance
(R.T.)

1. Oh, who — would be a shep - herd boy, And
mind — a flock of sheep, _____ While o - ther men and
boys en - joy A qui - et night of sleep? _____

2. Yes, who would choose to pass the night
   In darkness and in cold?
   Or hear the cry without a fright:
   The wolf is in the fold?

3. Now then there came a shining o.1e,
   An angel of the Lord;
   With news of God's eternal Son,
   By heavenly hosts adored.

4. 'The news,' said he, 'should make you glad,
   And fill your heart with joy;
   You'll find Him in a manger laid,
   A mother's Baby Boy.'

5. Then many more were heard to raise
   A cheerful hymn of mirth:
   'To God in heaven be endless praise;
   And peace to men on earth.'

6. The shepherds' hearts were comforted
   By what was told to them.
   'And after what we've heard,' they said,
   'Let's go to Bethlehem.'

John Gray

Sandys entitles the tune 'Lord Thomas' but gives no words to it.

31. IN BETHLEHEM CITY

Worcestershire melody
(R.T.)

1. In Beth - le - hem ci - ty, on Christ-mas day morn, Lord,
in a bare ca - vern Thou would-est be born: And
Thou, who for throne hast the hea - ven on high, Wast
fain in a ship-pon 'mid ox - en to lie.

2. And Thou, whom angelical troops aye surround,
   By certain poor herdsmen didst deign to be found,
   And this of Thy goodness, to rescue our race;
   So sing we, "All glory, and thanks for Thy grace."

3. And at the same season, behold, from afar
   There fared unto Bethlehem led by a star,
   Three princes of Saba, who knew by that sign
   That born upon earth was a monarch divine.

4. Choice treasure they bare Thee, myrrh, incense, and gold;
   And though Thou wert cradled 'mid beasts of the fold.
   They knelt, for they saw when they rendered Thee praise,
   The Son of the Father, the Ancient of Days.

G. R. Woodward

43

32. O THE MORN, THE MERRY, MERRY MORN

Traditional Air
(C.W.)

4. There within a cattle, cattle shed
   They find and worship him,
   Who rideth, in his realm o'erhead,
   Upon the Cherubim.

5. So, my boys, my bonny, bonny boys,
   To Bethlem off be we!
   But, pray you, shun whate'er annoys
   The Babe on Mary's knee.

G. R. Woodward

33. PAST THREE A CLOCK

Traditional
(C.W.)

Past three a clock, And a cold fro-sty morn-ing: Past three a clock; Good mor-row, mas-ters all!

1. Born is a Ba - by, Gen-tle as may be, Son of th'e - ter - nal Fa-ther su - per-nal. Past three a clock, *etc.*

2. Se - raph quire sing - eth, An-gel bell ring-eth: Hark how they rime it, Time it, and chime it.

3. Mid earth re - joic - es Hear-ing such voi-ces Ne'er-to - fore so well Ca-rol-ling *Now-ell.*

4. Hinds o'er the pearl - y Dew-y lawn ear - ly Seek the high stran-ger Laid in a man-ger.

5. Cheese from the dairy
Bring they for Mary,
And, not for money,
Butter and honey. *Refrain*

6. Light out of star-land
Leadeth from far land
Princes, to meet him,
Worship and greet him. *Refrain*

7. Myrrh from full coffer,
Incense they offer:
Nor is the golden
Nugget withholden. *Refrain*

8. Thus they: I pray you,
Up, sirs, nor stay you
Till ye confess him
Likewise, and bless him. *Refrain*

G. R. Woodward

The words of the refrain and the tune are found in Chappell: *Popular Music of Olden Time.*

34. AS I WENT TO BETHLEHEM

arr. by TREVOR WIDDICOMBE

from W. Byrd's setting of a traditional carol

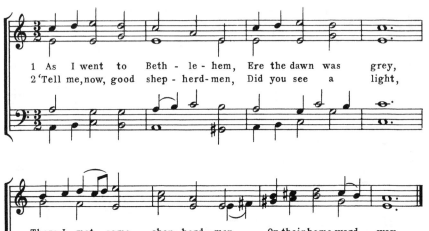

1 As I went to Beth - le - hem, Ere the dawn was grey,
2 'Tell me, now, good shep - herd- men, Did you see a light,

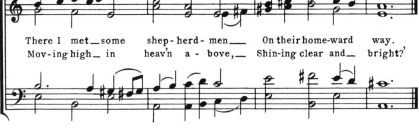

There I met — some shep - herd - men___ On their home-ward way.
Mov-ing high — in heav'n a - bove,___ Shin-ing clear and— bright?'

3　'When on yonder hill we stood,
　　Watching o'er our sheep,
　　Unto us an Angel spake,
　　While earth lay asleep:

4　'"Glory be to God," it said,
　　"And on earth be joy,
　　Unto you is born this day,
　　Christ the Holy boy."'

5　Forth we went to Bethlehem,
　　For to see the Child,
　　There he lay in Mary's arms,
　　Jesus meek and mild.

6　Then before the manger bed
　　We did kneel and pray,
　　Thanking God for His dear Son,
　　Born to us this day.

G. Hitchcock

35. THE BABE IN BETHL'EM'S MANGER LAID

c. 1800

1. The Babe in Beth-l'em's man-ger laid, In hum-ble form so low, By wond'ring an-gels is sur-vey'd Thro' all His scenes of woe.

REFRAIN

No - el, No - el, Loud sing a Sa-viour's birth, All hail His com-ing down to earth Who rais - es us to Heav'n.

2. A Saviour! sinners here around,
   Sing, shout the wondrous word;
   Let every bosom hail the sound,
   A Saviour! Christ the Lord.
   Noel, Noel, etc.

3. For not to sit on David's throne,
   With wordly pomp and joy;
   He came to earth for sin to atone,
   And Satan to destroy
   Noel, Noel, etc.

4. To preach the words of life divine,
   And feed with living bread,
   To heal the sick with hand benign,
   And raise to life the dead.
   Noel, Noel, etc.

5. Well may we sing a Saviour's birth,
   Who need the grace so given;
   And hail His coming down to earth,
   Who raises us to Heaven.
   Noel, Noel, etc.

This carol, whose words and music are clearly of the late eighteenth century, first appears in this complete form (with one more verse of words) in Rimbault's *Old English Carols*, (1865): but it appeared without the chorus in *A Good Christmas Box* (1847).

C

36. WHILE SHEPHERDS WATCHED

Dorset carol
collected by C. H. MAYO
(E.R.)

1 While shep-herds watched their flocks by night, All seat-ed on the ground, All seat - ed on the ground, The an-gel of the Lord came down, And glo-ry shone a - round, And glo-ry shone a - round, And glo - - - - ry shone a - round.

2 'Fear not,' said he (for migh - ty dread Had seized their trou-bled mind; Had seized their trou - bled mind); 'Glad ti-dings of great joy I bring To you and all man-kind, To you and all man-kind, To you and all man - kind!

3 'To you in David's town this day
Is born of David's line
A Saviour, who is Christ the Lord;
And this shall be the sign:

4 'The heavenly babe you there shall find
To human view displayed,
All meanly wrapped in swathing bands,
And in a manger laid.'

5 Thus spake the seraph: and forthwith
Appeared a shining throng
Of angels praising God, who thus
Addressed their joyful song:

6 'All glory be to God on high,
And to the earth be peace;
Goodwill henceforth from heaven to men
Begin and never cease'.

Nahum Tate (1652-1751)

48

37. WHILE SHEPHERDS WATCHED
(2nd tune)

Este's Psalter (1592)

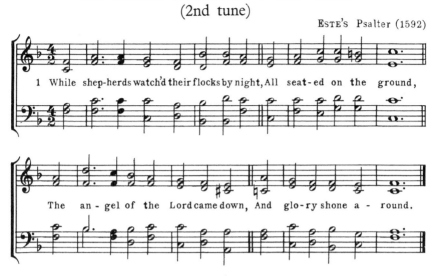

1 While shep-herds watch'd their flocks by night, All seat-ed on the ground,

The an - gel of the Lord came down, And glo-ry shone a - round.

2 'Fear not,' said he (for mighty dread
  Had seized their troubled mind);
  'Glad tidings of great joy I bring
  To you and all mankind'.

3 'To you in David's town this day
  Is born, of David's line,
  A Saviour, who is Christ the Lord;
  And this shall be the sign':

4 'The heavenly Babe you there shall find
  To human view displayed,
  All meanly wrapped in swathing bands,
  And in a manger laid'.

5 Thus spake the seraph; and forthwith
  Appeared a shining throng
  Of angels praising God, and thus
  Addressed their joyful song:

6 'All glory be to God on high,
  And to the earth be peace;
  Goodwill henceforth from heaven to men
  Begin and never cease!'

Nahum Tate (1652-1751)

38. THE OLD HARK

Leicestershire melody
(E. R.)

1 Hark! Hark! Hark! hark what news the An-gels bring, Glad
Hark! Hark! Glad

Glad ti-dings, Glad ti-dings, Glad ti-dings of a new-born King.
ti-dings, Glad ti-dings, Glad ti-dings of a new - born King.
Glad, Glad ti-dings of a new - born King.

Who is the Sa - viour of man-kind, In whom we may
Who is the Sa - viour of man - kind, In whom we may sal-
Who is the Sa - viour of man - kind, In

sal-va-tion find, In whom we may sal-va-tion find.
-va-tion find, In whom we may sal - va - tion find.

2 This is the day, the blessed morn,
The Saviour of mankind was born,
Born of a maid, a virgin pure,
Born without sin, from guilt secure.

3 If angels sang at Jesus' birth,
Sure we have greater cause for mirth,
For why it was then for our sakes,
Christ did our human nature take.

4 Sweet Christ, Thou did'st Thyself debase,
Thus to descend to human race,
And leave Thy Father's throne above,
Lord, what could move Thee to this love.

5 May we contemplate and admire,
And join with the celestial choir,
Extend your voice above the sky,
"All glory be to God on high."

50

39. THE OLD HARK
(2nd tune)

18th century tune
(R.T.)

1 Hark! hark what news the An - gels bring, Glad ti-dings of a new_____ born King; Who is the Sa - viour__ of man - kind, In whom we may sal - va - - - - - tion find

2 This is the day, the blessed morn,
  The Saviour of mankind was born,
  Born of a maid, a virgin pure,
  Born without sin, from guilt secure.

3 If angels sang at Jesus' birth,
  Sure we have greater cause for mirth,
  For why it was then for our sakes,
  Christ did our human nature take.

4 Sweet Christ, Thou did'st Thyself debase,
  Thus to descend to human race,
  And leave Thy Father's throne above,
  Lord, what could move Thee to this love.

5 May we contemplate and admire,
  And join with the celestial choir,
  Extend your voice above the sky,
  "All glory be to God on high."

This tune appears in Sandys, and was probably well known in the West Country as a setting for these words.

40. COME, TUNE YOUR CHEERFUL VOICE
(Dorset Carol)

(W. A. P-C.)

1 Come, tune your cheer-ful voice, Loud an-thems let us sing,— For un-to us is born to-day, For un-to us— is born to-day, A Sa-viour and a King— For un-to us— is born to-day, A Sa-viour and— a King, A Sa-viour and a King.

2 Hark, what a joyful sound
Re-echoes from above,
The Angels singing praise to God
For His redeeming love!

3 All hail our Saviour God!
Due thanks before Him pay,
For His great mercies shown to men
On this auspicious day.

4 "All glory be to God"
Aloud let Angels sing!
For unto us is born to-day
A Saviour and a King.

Traditional

52

41. AWAKE, AND JOIN THE CHEERFUL CHOIR

Melody by T. JARMAN, 1776-1861
(W. A. P-C.)

1. A - wake, and join___ the cheer-ful Choir, Up - on this joy-ful morn, up - on___ this joy-ful morn, And glad Ho - san - nas loud - ly sing. For joy a Saviour's born, For joy a Saviour's born, For joy a Saviour's born, For joy a Saviour's joy a Sav-iour's born, For joy a Sav - iour's born.

born,___ For___ joy, for___ joy___ a___ Sav - iour's born.
born, For joy, for___ joy___ a___ Sav - iour's born.
born, For___ joy,___ for___ joy___ a___ Sav - iour's born.

2. The shining host in bright array
   Descends from Heaven to earth:
   And joyful news to us they bring
   Of our dear Saviour's birth.

3. Let all the choirs on earth below
   Their voices loudly raise;
   And gladly join the cheerful band
   Of angels in the skies.

4. But let us join the cheerful song
   With joy and pious mirth,
   And all with grateful heart and voice
   Proclaim the Saviour's birth.

This well known Methodist hymn tune was first published in Jarman's *Sacred Music* (c. 1803).
Its cheerful style is especially oppropriate to the carol. (*cf. The English Carol*, pp 144 f).

53

42. A CHILD MY CHOICE
Let folly praise

English traditional
(R.T.)

1 Let fol - ly praise what fan-cy loves, I praise and love that Child, Whose heart no thought, whose tongue no__ word__ Whose hand no deed__ de - filed, I praise Him most, I love Him best, All__ praise and love is His; While

Him I love, in Him I live, And can-not live a - miss.

2   Love's sweetest mark, laud's highest theme,
      Man's most desired delight;
      To love Him life, to leave Him death,
      To live in Him delight.
        He mine by gift, I His by debt,
        Thus each to other due,
        First friend He was, best friend He is,
        All times will find Him true.

3   Though young yet wise, though small yet strong,
      Though Man yet God He is ;
      As wise He knows, as strong He can,
      As God He loves to bless.
        His knowledge rules, His strength defends,
        His love doth cherish all;
        His birth our joy, His life our light,
        His death our end of thrall.

4   Alas! He weeps, He sighs, He pants,
      Yet do His angels sing ;
      Out of His tears, His sighs, and throbs
      Doth bud a joyful spring.
        Almighty Babe, Whose tender arms
        Can force all foes to fly,
        Correct my faults, protect my life,
        Direct me when I die.

Robert Southwell
c. 1561 - 95

43. NEW PRINCE, NEW POMPE

English traditional
(C.W.)

1 Be - houlde a se - ly ten - der Babe In free - sing win - ter nighte,___ In home - ly man - ger trem - bling lies: A - las, a pi - tious sighte: The inns are full, no man will yelde This lit - tle Pil - grime bedd: But

56

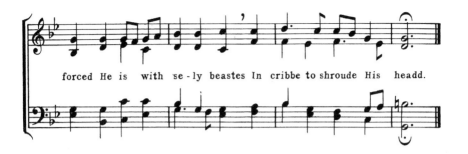

forced He is with se-ly beastes In cribbe to shroude His headd.

2 Despise not Him for lying there,
   First what He is enquire:
   An orient perle is often found
   In depth of dirty mire.
   Waye not His cribbe, His wodden dishe,
   Nor beastes that by Him feede:
   Waye not His Mother's poore attire,
   Nor Josephe's simple weede.

3 This stable is a Prince's courte,
   The cribbe His chaire of state:
   The beastes are parcell of His pompe,
   The wodden dishe His plate.
   The parsons in that poor attire
   His royall liveries weare:
   The Prince Himself is come from heaven,
   This pompe is prised there.

4 With joye approch, O Christen wighte,
   Do homage to thy Kinge:
   And highly prise this humble pompe,
   Which He from heaven doth bringe:
   With joye approch, O Christen wighte,
   Do homage to thy Kinge:
   And highly prise this humble pompe
   Which He from heaven doth bringe.

Robert Southwell, c.1561-95

This tune has had a varied history, and is clearly one of the most popular of English Ballad tunes. The above version is that set to 'We are poor frozen-out gardeners' in Chappell: but another form is found in Ireland set to 'The Star of County Down,' and another, associated with the carol 'Job,' has been used in modern times as a hymn tune (O.B.C.60, cf E.H.574). See E.C.

44. A LUTE LULLABY

JOHN DOWLAND

1. Lul - lay my babe, lie still and sleep, Soar it grieves me to
thou be qui - et I'd be glad, Weep - ing thus makes

hear thee weep, Would'st me so sad. My pret - ty lamb,

my pret - ty boy, Sweet - ly sleep, Je - su my Joy. My lit - tle Son,

my lit - tle King, Oh! would'st thou wert peace - ful - ly sleep - ing.

2. Oh! would'st some angel kiss thy brow,
   Sing lullay, sing balalow,
   While thus thy lullaby I sing,
   Music soothe my sweet lording.
   My pretty lamb, *etc.*

3. What ails my darling thus to cry,
   Sing lullay, sing lullaby,
   Lie still, my darling rest awhile,
   When thou wakest sweetly smile.
   My pretty lamb, *etc.*

16th cent. (altd.)

58

45. SING WE, THEN, MERRILY

WILLIAM BYRD
from "Queen Elizabeth's Virginal Book"
(G. G.)

1. Je-sus so meek, Je-sus so mild, Je-sus was
   In man-ger rude, Fil-lèd with hay, Je-sus our
   once— a lit-tle child,
   Sa-viour gent-ly lay.

REFRAIN.

Sing we, then, mer-ri-ly, mer-ri-ly, sing no-well, Sing we to Jes-us, Em-man-u-el.

2. Mary so sweet, Mary so true,
   May we all gentle be just like you.
   Soften our hearts, make us all kind
   Then in our hearts a home Jesus find.
   Sing we then, *etc.*

3. Joseph so brave, Joseph so fine
   Father of Jesus, the Babe Divine,
   Teach us to grow healthy and strong,
   That we may work for God all day long.
   Sing we then, *etc.*

4. Kings from afar at his feet fall,
   In homage kneel by the asses stall.
   From Bethle'ms hills, come shepherds come,
   Haste to your Saviour's humble home.
   Sing we then, *etc.*

5. Come children all, sing out his praise,
   Carol the Infant in sweetest lays.
   Let us our hearts Gifts to him bring,
   Ever to honour and serve our King.
   Sing we then, *etc.*

G. Grimes

This carol is suitable for antiphonal singing.

46. I SING THE BIRTH

Melody by M. PRAETORIUS, 1571-1621
(E. R.)

1 I sing the birth was born to-night, The au-thor both of life and light; The an-gels so— did sound— it; And like the va-nish'd shep-herds said, Who saw the light and wert a-fraid, Yet staunch and true they found— it.

2 The Son of God, th'Eternal King,
That did us all salvation bring,
   And freed our soul from danger,
He whom the whole world could not take,
The Word, which heaven and earth did make,
   Was now laid in a manger.

3 The Father's wisdom willed it so,
The Son's obedience knew no No,
   Both wills were in one stature,
And, as that wisdom had decreed,
The Word was now made flesh indeed,
   And took on him our nature.

4 What comfort by him do we win,
Who made himself the price of sin,
   To make us heirs of glory!
To see this Babe, all innocence,
A martyr born in our defence,
   Can man forget the story?

Ben Jonson, 1573-1637

47. LORD, WHEN THE WISE MEN CAME

Paris *Antiphoner*, 1681
(E. R.)

1 Lord, when the wise men came from far,
Led to thy cradle by a star,
Shepherds with humble fearfulness
Walked safely, though their light was less.

2 Wise men in tracing Nature's laws
Ascend unto the highest cause:
Though wise men better know the way,
It seems no honest heart can stray.

3 And since no creature comprehends
The Cause of causes, End of ends,
He who himself vouchsafes to know
Best pleases his Creator so.

4 There is no merit in the wise,
But love, the shepherds' sacrifice:
Wise men, all ways of knowledge past,
To the shepherds' wonder came at last.

cento from Sidney Godolphin, 1610-43

The poem from which these lines are selected may be found at No. 138 of the *Oxford Book of Christian Verse*.

48. AT THE NATIVITY

Alsatian Cradle Song, 1697
(R.T.)

1 Gloom - y night_ em-braced the place Where-in __ the no - ble

In - fant lay; ___ The_ Babe look'd up ___ and shew'd His face, In

spite_ of dark - ness it ___ was day! It was ___ Thy day, Sweet!

and ___ did rise, Not from __ the east, __ but from __ Thine eyes.

*The notes in brackets will not be sung in verses 1 and 2

62

2 Winter chid aloud, and sent
  The angry North to wage his wars.
 The North forgot his fierce intent,
  And left perfumes instead of scars.
 By those sweet eyes' persuasive powers
 Where he meant frost, he scattered flowers.

3 We saw Thee in Thy balmy nest,
  Young Dawn of our eternal day!
 We saw Thine eyes break from their east
  And chase the trembling shades away,
 We saw Thee; and we blessed the sight,
 We saw Thee by Thine Own sweet light.

4 Welcome, all wonders in one sight!
  Eternity shut in a span!
 Summer in winter, day in night!
  Heaven in earth, and God in man!
 Great little one! Whose lowly birth,
 Lifts earth to heav'n, stoops Heav'n to earth.

5 To Thee, meek Majesty! soft King
  Of simple graces and sweet loves;
 Each one of us his lamb will bring,
  And each his pair of silver doves;
 Till burnt in fire of Thy fair eyes,
 Ourselves become our sacrifice!

cento from
Richard Crashaw c. 1613-49

49. A SHOOT, A SHOOT ON JESSE'S TREE

Nursery Rhyme "Miss Lucy"
(G. H.)

2 This shoot shall grow a goodly tree,
   An holy vine and true,
   Wherein whoe'er engrafted be
   Is born and lives anew.

3 And fruit that noble tree shall bear,
   And like the manna shed,
   For men shall pluck thee as they fare,
   The true and living Bread.

Words by A. Religious of C. S. M. V.

50. THE SUN IN THE MORNING

Sussex folk song
(E.R.)

1 O I sing of a sim-ple sta-ble in an inn - yard so ___
2 And I sing of some shep-herds watch-ing o'er their sheep by ___
3 And I sing of God's love ___ to his own cre-a - ted ___

small Where the ox - en and the as - ses they are watch-ing by a
night, When there came an an-gel to them all clo - thèd in
earth, As for us poor men of sin was his own Son giv-en

stall. Where lies the maid-en Ma - ry by a man-ger of
light. Glad ti - dings of great joy did he un - to them
birth. Let us all sing and re-joice in his love and be

hay And the
say And the { sun in the morn-ing shall rise on Christ-mas day.
gay For the

Philippa Renwick

65

51. GLORY TO GOD IN HEIGHTS OF HEAVEN

Wiltshire melody
(R.T.)

1. Glo - ry to God in heights of heaven; Glo -
2. Ah Lord! and whence to us is this? Our

- ry to God; on earth be peace; For God hath made Him
sin we know, and know Thy grace; But dost Thou dwell with

Man for men, And earth's cap-tiv - i - ties shall cease.
us in - deed? Shall these dark eyes be - hold Thy face?

3. Might not the Lord of Thrones and Powers
    Send earth some bright archangel down
  To lift the fallen race, and set
    On mortal brows the immortal crown?

4. Not so Thy mercy rests; not so
    Thy courtesy shall be sufficed;
  Love's measure may be nought but love;
    Christ will not offer less than Christ.

5. The quiring angels down the sky
    Sing for the joy that comes to men;
  And we to whom it comes, might we
    Give angel-answer back again.

W. H. Shewring

52. WHEN CHRIST WAS BORN OF MARY FREE

TREVOR WIDDICOMBE

1 When Christ was born of Ma-ry free In Beth-le-hem that

V.2 Herds-men be-held these an-gels bright to them ap-pear-ed
V.3 Then, dear Lord, in thy great grace Grant us in bliss to

fair ci - ty: An-gels sung e'er with mirth and glee:

with great light, And said; "God's son is born to night."
see thy face, Where we may sing to thy so - lace:

In — ex - cel - sis, in — ex - cel - sis glor - i - a,

in ex - cel - sis glor - - i - a.

Harleian MS. 1456

53. MYN LYKING

RICHARD TERRY

1 I saw a fair may - den syt-tin and sing. She lul - led a lyt-tel childe, a sweeté lord - ing.

2 That same Lord is he that made al - lé thing Of al - le lord-is He is Lord of al - lé kynges Kyng.

CHORUS
Lul - lay myn lyk-ing, my dere sonne, my sweet-ing. Lul - lay my dere herte, myn

Lul - la - lay. Lul - la-lay. Lul-lay my dere herte, myn

Lul-la - lay. Lul-la - lay. Lul - lay myn

Sloane MS. A.D. 1396

54. I SING OF A MAYDEN

RICHARD TERRY

1 I sing of a may-den That is make-les, The
King of all king-es, To her sone she ches. He
came all so still-é There his mo-ther was, As
dew in Ap-ril-lé That fall'th on the grass.

2 He came all so stillé
   To his mother's bower,
   As dew in Aprillé
   That fall'th on the flower.
   He came all so stillé
   There his mother lay,
   As dew in Aprillé
   That fall'th on the spray.

Sloane MS.

55. THOU, WHOSE BIRTH ON EARTH

From a Tournai MS.
(E. P.)

1. Thou, whose birth on earth, — An-gels sang — to — men.
While Thy stars made mirth, Sav-iour at — Thy — birth,
This — day — born — a - gain. —

2. As this night was bright, With Thy cradle-ray,
Very light of light, Turn the wild world's night,
To Thy perfect day.

3. Thou the Word and Lord, In all time and space
Heard, beheld, adored, With all ages poured
Forth before Thy face.

4. Lord, what worth in earth Drew Thee down to die?
What therein was worth, Lord, Thy death and birth?
What beneath the sky?

5. Yet Thy poor endure, And are with us yet?
Be Thy Name a sure refuge for the poor.
Though men's eyes forget.

6. Bid our peace increase, Thou Who madest morn;
Bid oppressions cease; Bid there cometh peace,
Thou, this day born again.

A.C.Swinburne

71

56. SEE AMID THE WINTER'S SNOW

John Goss, 1800–1880

1. See a-mid the win-ter's snow, Born for us on earth be-low,
See the ten-der Lamb ap-pears, Promised from e-ter-nal years.

REFRAIN (Full)

Hail! thou ev-er bless-ed morn! Hail, re-demp-tion's hap-py dawn!
Sing thro' all Je-ru-sa-lem, Christ is born in Beth-le-hem.

2. Lo, within a manger lies
   He who built the starry skies;
   He, who throned in height sublime,
   Sits amid the Cherubim!
   Hail! thou ever blessèd morn! etc.

3. Say, ye holy Shepherds, say,
   What your joyful news to-day;
   Wherefore have ye left your sheep
   On the lonely mountain steep?
   Hail! thou ever blessèd morn! etc.

4. 'As we watched at dead of night,
   Lo, we saw a wondrous light;
   Angels singing peace on earth,
   Told us of a Saviour's birth.'
   Hail! thou ever blessèd morn! etc.

5. Sacred Infant, all divine,
   What a tender love was thine;
   Thus to come from highest bliss
   Down to such a world as this!
   Hail! thou ever blessèd morn! etc.

6. Teach, O teach us, Holy Child,
   By thy face so meek and mild,
   Teach us to resemble Thee,
   In Thy sweet humility!
   Hail! thou ever blessèd morn! etc.

Edward Caswall

57. THE ANGELS SING AROUND THE STALL

RICHARD TERRY

1 The an-gels sing a - round the stall where Je-sus cra-dled lies: The
shep-herds hear the joy-ful call That wakes the si - lent_ skies. Hark
to the mu - sic float-ing by, ere yet its e - choes cease,—— Poured
ere yet its e-choes cease,
forth by an-gels min-strel-sy, Is heard the song of peace.
Is heard the song of peace.

2   The eastern kings the star have seen
      They hasten on their way;
   Long time they've watched and waiting been
      The dawning of that day,
   The dawning of that day of grace,
      The gleam of Jacob's star,
   The Virgin's Child, of Jesse's race,
      Whom prophets saw afar.

3   And now they open treasures rare
      That Indian silks enfold,
   Of myrrh that sweetly scents the air,
      Of frankincense, and gold.
   Their kingly heads they meekly bow
      The cradled Babe before;
   Their God confess and, kneeling low,
      In humble faith adore.

4   With them I come to greet my King,
      Yet not with them to part;
   No gold, no frankincense I bring,
      I offer him my heart.
   With him to live, with him to die,
      Who by his lowly birth
   Gave glory to our God on high,
      And peace to men on earth.

Peter Gallwey

58. HOW FAR IS IT TO BETHLEHEM?

West Country Carol
(E.R.)

1 How far is it to Beth-le-hem? Not ve-ry far.
3 May we stroke the crea-tures there Ox, ass or sheep?
5 Great kings have pre-cious gifts, and we have naught

Shall we__ find the sta-ble room lit by a star?
May we__ peep like them and see Je-sus a-sleep?
Lit-tle smiles and lit-tle tears are all__ we brought.

2 Can we see the lit-tle child, Is he with-in?
4 If we touch his ti-ny hand, will he a-wake?
6 For all wea-ry chil-dren Ma-ry must weep,
7 God's in his mo-ther's arms; Babes in the byre,

D. ℅ for v. 7

If we lift the wood-en latch, may we go in?
Will he know we've come so far just for his sake?
Here on his bed of straw, sleep, chil-dren sleep.
Sleep, as they sleep who find their heart's de-sire.

★ tenor sings A♭ in v. 5

Frances Chesterton

† all parts hold chord 3 beats in vv 6 and 7, omitting the rest of the notes in this bar.

59. THE CHRIST-CHILD LAY

Melody from Corner's *Geistliche Gesangbuch*, 1649
(R.T.)

The Christ-child lay on Mary's lap,

1 His
2 His
3 His
4 His

hair was like a light, (O wea - ry, wea - ry
hair was like a star. (O stern and cun - ning

hair was like a fire. (O wea - ry, wea - ry
hair was like a crown, And all the flow'rs look'd

were the world, But here is all a -
are the Kings, But here the true hearts

is the world, But here the world's de -
up at Him And all the stars look'd

right,) _____ (But here is all a - right.)
are.) _____ (But here the true hearts are.)

- sire.) (But here the world's de - sire.)
down. (And all the stars look'd down.)

G. K. Chesterton

60. MASTERS IN THIS HALL

French carol (Chartres)
(T. W.)

1. Mas-ters in this Hall,— Hear ye news to-day— Brought from o - ver sea,— And ev - er I you pray: Now-ell! Now-ell! Now - ell! Now - ell sing we clear! Holp-en are all folk on earth,— Born— is God's son so dear:

This long carol is useful as a processional: the verses should be varied (i.e. men in unison, boys in unison, full unison & S.A.T.B.) as desired.

Now - ell! Now - ell!

Now - ell! Now - ell!___ Now - ell sing we loud! God to -

- day hath poor folk raised And___ cast a - down the proud.

2. Going o'er the hills,
   Through the milk-white snow,
   Heard I ewes bleat
   While the wind did blow:

3. Shepherds many an one
   Sat among the sheep,
   No man spake more word
   Than they had been asleep:

4. Quoth I, 'Fellows mine,
   Why this guise sit ye?
   Making but dull cheer,
   Shepherds though ye be?'

5. Shepherds should of right
   Leap and dance and sing
   Thus to see ye sit,
   Is a right strange thing':

6. Quoth these fellows then,
   'To Bethlem town we go,
   To see a mighty lord
   Lie in manger low':

7. 'How name ye this lord,
   Shepherds?' then said I,
   'Very God,' they said,
   'Come from Heaven high':

8. Then to Bethlem town
   We went two and two,
   And in a sorry place
   Heard the oxen low:

9. Therein did we see
   A sweet and goodly may
   And a fair old man,
   Upon the straw she lay:

10. And a little child
    On her arm had she,
    'Wot ye who this is?'
    Said the hinds to me:

11. Ox and ass him know,
    Kneeling on their knee,
    Wondrous joy had I
    This little babe to see:

12. This is Christ the Lord,
    Masters be ye glad!
    Christmas is come in,
    And no folk should be sad:

William Morris

61. IN THE BLEAK MID-WINTER

GUSTAV HOLST, 1874-1934

1. • In the bleak mid - win - ter Frost - y wind made moan,

2. Our God, heav'n can-not hold him, Nor___ earth sus - tain; •
3. E - nough for him,whom Cher-u-bim Wor-ship night and day, A
4. • An - gels and Arch-an - gels May have gath-er'd there, •
5. • What___ can I give him, Poor___ as I am •

Earth stood hard as Ir - on, Wa - ter like a stone;

2. Heav'n and earth shall flee a-way • When he comes to reign: •
3. breast - ful of milk And a man-ger-ful of hay; E -
4. Cher - u - bim and Ser - a-phim • Throng'd ___ the air, But
5. If I were a shep - herd • I would bring a lamb; •

Snow had fal - len, snow on snow, Snow___ on ___ snow,

2. In the bleak mid - win - ter A sta - ble place suf - fic'd The
3. -nough for him, whom An - gels • Fall___ down be - fore, The
4. on - ly his moth - er • In her maid-en bliss •
5. If I were a wise man • I would do my part Yet

In the bleak mid - win - ter, Long_____ a - go.

2. Lord___ God al - might - y Je - sus Christ.
3. ox and ass and cam - el Which ___ a - dore.
4. Wor-shipp'd the Bel - o - vèd With ___ a kiss.
5. what I can I give him— Give _____ my heart.

Christina Rossetti

80

62. LOVE CAME DOWN AT CHRISTMAS

LOVE INCARNATE

EDGAR PETTMAN
With added Noël

1. Love came down at Christmas, Love all love-ly, Love Divine; Love was born at Christmas, Star and angels gave the sign. Sing Noël, Sing Noël, Sing Noël, Sing Noël. Sing Noël, Sing Noël.

2. Worship we the Godhead,
   Love incarnate, Love Divine;
   Worship we our Jesus:
   But wherewith for sacred sign?

3. Love shall be our token,
   Love be yours and love be mine;
   Love to God and all men,
   Love for plea, and gift and sign.

Christina G. Rossetti

81

63. A CAROL OF ADORATION

EDGAR PETTMAN, 1867-1943

Slowly and softly

1. O Babe Di-vine, now will I sing To Thee a song of love - long - ing: Make in my heart a quick well-spring, Thy - self to love a - bove all thing.

2. O Holy Child, my dim heart's gleam,
O brighter than the sunny beam!
As Thou wast born in Bethlehem,
Be born in me and be my dream.

3. O Prince of Peace, my dark soul's light!
Thou art a day without a night:
O give me strength and give me might
Ever to love Thyself aright.

4. O Son of God, Thou warrior best!
Thy love, Thou in mine heart make fast;
When I go North, South, East or West
In Thee alone may I find rest.

5. Jesu, it well for him shall be
That in Thy bliss Thyself shall see:
O then with love-chords draw Thou me,
That I may come and dwell with Thee.

Old English, modernised and adapted by
W. A. Pickard-Cambridge.

64. LO! UNTO US A CHILD IS BORN

Words and Music by   REGINALD GIBBS-SMITH

1 Lo! un - to us a child is born, The Lord of Life and Love!
To call us all this Christ - mas Morn, To hap - pi - ness a - bove.

2 Then Ca - rols sing, good Chris - tians all, With An - gel hosts a - bove
For Christ we keep the fes - ti - val, And Je - sus owns our love.

3 And thus let all the ran - somed earth Re - sound with har - mo - ny;
For our Re - deem - er's hum - ble Birth Laud we the One in Three.

65. CLEAN AS THE WIND

Graham Foulkes

Allegretto

mp 1. Clean as the wind that bends— the bough

Wash— me now, for Je - sus; Clean as the mid - night

wind that swept O - ver the stall where Je - sus slept.

2. Warm as our winter fireside's light
   Let me burn bright, for Jesus;
   Warm as the love that Mary shed
   Round our Saviour's manger bed.

3. Strong as the joy of Christmas Eve
   I believe in Jesus.
   Strength came to men when Jesus smiled,
   God's whole Presence in a child.

4. Clean, warm and strong, O King Divine,
   Make my heart shine, for Jesus;
   Shine with the Angel's glory bright
   Fill the world with Christmas light.

Richard E. Horn

66. WHENCE IS THAT GOODLY FRAGRANCE

PATRICK FORBES

A. B. Ramsay

67. A CHRISTMAS LULLABY

Clifford Curwin

Through the door a lit-tle o-pen Howled a bit-ter wind un-bro-ken. Then appeared the three wise men Wending their way to Beth-le-hem, Gaz-ing at the star a-bove, Read-y to give Him gifts of love. Diane Bennetto

87

D*

68 IF CHRIST WERE BORN IN BURNLEY

MAURICE LEAH
(E.R.)

1 If Christ were born in Burn-ley This Christ-mas night, This Christ-mas night; I know not if the moors would shine With heav'n-ly light, With heav'n-ly light. But this I know, My heart would glow, And all its in-ner ra-diance show, If Christ were born in Burn-ley.

2 If Christ were born in Burnley
This Christmas-tide,
This Christmas-tide;
I know not if with treasures rare
The wise would ride,
The wise would ride.
But I would bring
My offering,
To kneel and worship hastening;
If Christ were born in Burnley.

3 If Christ were born in Burnley
This Christmas day,
This Christmas day;
I know not if the busy throng
Would bid Him stay,
Would bid Him stay.
But He might rest,
My heart's own guest,
Of praise and glory worthiest;
If Christ were born in Burnley.

A. F. Bayly

These words were written by Mr. Bayly when he was a minister in Burnley. The local reference gives point to the carol, but any place name that is metrically suitable may be substituted. If any sense of incongruity occurs to the singer, it should be remembered that this is the essence of one form of the traditional carol. Those who live in places whose names do not fit the rhythm may sing 'In my town.'

69. COVENTRY CAROL

From the Coventry Tailors'
and Shearmen's pageant

(R. T.)

1 Lul - ly, lul - la, you lit - tle ti - ny child;
2 O sis - ters too how may we do

3 He - rod the King in his ra - ging,
4 That woe is me, poor Child, for Thee

By, by, lul - ly, lul - lay. You lit - tle ti - ny child; Lul -
For to pre - serve this day, This poor young - ling, For

Charg - ed he hath this day, His men of might, In
And ev - er mourn and say, For Thy part - ing, Nor

- ly, __ lul - la; By, by, lul - ly, __ lul - lay.
whom __ we sing By, by, lul - ly, __ lul - lay?

his __ own sight, All child - ren __ young to __ slay.
say __ nor sing By, by, lul - ly, __ lul - lay.

This is a modern version of the next carol

89

70. COVENTRY CAROL
(Ancient version)

whom we do— sing, by by, lul - ly lul - lay.

say— nor— sing by by, lul - ly lul - lay.

Unison   4   (E.R.)

2 *f* He - rod the king in his ra - ging charg-ed he
(*attacca*)

hath this day his men of might in his own

sight All young chil - dren to slay.

ff

D.%

* This tenor note is written F♮ in the original. Good choirs may attempt that version.

† This direction applies only when the unison version of v. 2 is sung.

This version combines the original 3-part harmony of 1591 with a modern setting of verse 2, designed to represent the profane intrusion of Herod into the sacred scene: Verses 1 and 3 should be sung by a trio, or a small group, unaccompanied ; verse 2 should be sung by all available voices in unison, and may be accompanied by an organ, using Swell 16 foot reed and mixture.

71. HAIL MARY, FULL OF GRACE

15th cent.
(R.T.)

(1) These small notes are missing in the MS.(R.R. Terry.)

D.C.

- in   thee   went,   (2) While   the   an-gel   said 'A   -   *ve.'*

God   and   Man,   [Through] vir-tue through   dig-ni   -   ty.(3)

3   So saith the gospel of Saint John;
    (That) God and man is made but one,
    [In] flesh and blood, body and bone;
    One God in Personès Three.

4   And the (high) prophet Jeremy,
    Told (all men) in his prophecy
    That the Son of Mary (free)
    Should die for us on rood tree.

5   Much joy to us was then y-grant,
    And in the earth was peace y-plant,
    When that born was this Infant,
    In the land of Galilee.

6   (Maid) Mary grant to us the bliss
    Where thy (dere) Sonnès dwelling is.
    Of that we have done amiss
    Pray for us for charity.

Words and melody from a parchment roll in the library of Trinity College, Cambridge. 15th cent.
(2) The word 'while' and the melody note belonging to it are not in the MS.   They are inserted here because *(a)* both occur in the Bodleian MS. version. *(b)* the phrase does not carry its real sense without the omitted word. *(c)* without extra note there are too few notes to carry the syllables of the verbal text.   I have assumed a copyist's omission; it is open to anyone (after comparison of the two MSS.) to disagree with me.
(3) The MS. gives *'your* dignity.' The Bodleian version gives the line 'Through the virtue of *the* dignity.' I have therefore assumed a copyist's miswriting(in the Trinity College MS.) of y for p (a not uncommon mistake). If this be so, it should read 'powr,' – a rare but not impossible form of 'prow,' 'porw,' *i.e.* 'through'. [R.R.T.]
Went- gone. *Y-grant*-granted. *Y-plant*-plenty.

72. WHAT TIDINGS BRINGEST THOU, MESSENGER?

15th cent.
(R.T.)

REFRAIN

What ti - dings bring-est thou, mes-sen-ger, Of Christ-ès
birth this joy-ful day? 1 A Babe is born of high na-

VERSES

-ture, The Prince of Peace that ev-er shall be, Of hea-ven and
earth He— hath the— cure, His lord-ship is e - ter-ni-

(1) At each of the points marked with an asterisk the MS. gives two beats' rest,- destroying
the rhythmic continuity of the tune. As no such rests occur in the Bodleian copy, I have
omitted them here.

94

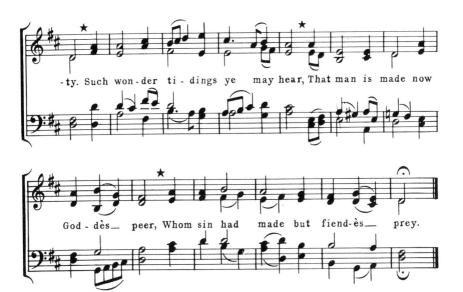

-ty. Such won-der ti-dings ye may hear, That man is made now God-dès_ peer, Whom sin had made but fiend-ès_ prey.

2 A wonder-thing is now befall;
   That King that formed star and sun,
   Heaven and earth and angels all,
   Now in mankind is new begun.
     Such wonder-tidings ye may hear,
     A Faunt is now of (but) one year,
     That hath been ever and shall be aye.

3 That seemliest selkouth[1] to see,
   This bird that hath this Babe yborn
   And Lord conceived of high degree
   A maiden is, as was beforn.
     Such wonder-tidings ye may hear,
     That maiden and mother is one in fere,
     And she a Lady of great array.

4 That loveliest gan greet her child,
   'Hail Son! Hail Brother! Hail Father dear!
   Hail daughter![2] Hail sister! Hail mother mild!'
   This hailing was in quaint mannèr
     Such wonder-tidings ye may hear,
     That hailing was of so good cheer
     That mannès pain[3] is turned to play.

Words and melody from a parchment roll in the library of Trinity College, Cambridge. 15th cent.
(1) I have retained this line exactly as in MS. on account of its scansion. *Selkouth*-to make wonderful.
(2)'He saith' occurs in the MS. after this word. As its insertion would make the line unsingable
by the average choir I have omitted it.
(3) Between 'mannes' and 'pain' the MS. has 'syne' (sin) very doubtfully erased. It looks as though
the writer at first wrote 'syne' and then changed his mind and wrote 'peyn' instead, in order
to keep the alliteration, forgetting to erase 'syne' completely. [R.R.T.]
Cure- care, charge. *Faunt*- infant. *Beforn*- before. *Bird*- girl, maid. *Infere*-together.

73. TIDINGS TRUE

SELDEN M.S. c. 1450
(E.R.)

No - well, No - well, No - well, No - well, This is the

sa - lu - ta - tion of the an - gel Ga - bri - el.

1 Ti - dings true there be come new sent from the Tri - ni -

-ty_____ By Ga - bri - el to Na - za - reth Ci - ty of

Ga - li - lee._____ A pure vir - gin, and low - ly

maid Through her hu - mi - li - ty ——— Hath now con- ceiv'd the Per - son se - cond in De - i - ty. ———

2   When that he presented was before her fair visage
In most demure and goodly wise he did to her homage;
And said, 'Lady from heaven so high, that Lordes heritage,
For he of thee now born will be; I'm sent on his message.'

3   'Hail virgin celestial, the meek'st that ever was!
Hail, temple of the Deity! Hail mirror of all grace!
Hail virgin pure! I thee ensure within a little space
Thou shalt conceive and him receive that shall bring great solace.'

4   Then bespoke the maid again and answered womanly,
'Whate'er my Lord commandeth me I will obey truly.'
With *ecce sum humillima ancilla Domini:*
Secundum verbum tuum, she said, *Fiat mihi.*

v. 4. The Latin passage means: 'Behold I am the humblest handmaid of the Lord. According to thy word' (she said) 'be it done unto me.'

The first verse is in the Selden MS. The others come from various traditional sources.

74. MAKE WE JOY NOW IN THIS FEST

Mode IX

Medieval Church Carol
(R.T.)

come.   Ve - ni   Re - dem-ptor   gen - ci - um.

Ve - ni

Ve - ni

2 *Agnoscat omne seculum,*
  A bright star maketh three kinges come,
  Him for to seek with their presents.
  Verbum supernum prodiens.

3 *A solis ortus cardine,*
  So mighty a Lord was none as He;
  For to our kind He hath given peace,
  Adam parens quod polluit.

4 *Maria ventre concepit,*
  The Holy Ghost was aye here with;
  In Bethlehem y-born He is,
  Consors Paterni luminis

5 *O lux beata Trinitas,*
  He lay between an ox and ass,
  Thou mother pure and maiden free.
  Gloria tibi Domine.

The Latin tags are lines from hymns well known in the Middle ages: some of them are still
known in English translation.

  v. 1 'The Father's sole-begotten Son' (A. & M. 486)
        'Come, thou Redeemer of the earth' (E.H. 14)
  v. 2 'Let every age acknowledge him'
        'High Word of God proceeding forth' (E.H. 2)
  v. 3 'From East to West, from shore to shore' (E.H. 18)
        'What Adam our father corrupted'
  v. 4 'Mary conceived in her womb'
        'Co-equal with the father's light'
  v. 5 'O Trinity of blessed light' (E.H. 164)
        'Glory to thee, O Lord'

75. THERE IS NO ROSE

Mode I

Words and melody from a parchment roll in the
library of Trinity College, Cambridge (15th cent.)
(R.T.)

REFRAIN

1 There is no rose of such vir - tue As is the— rose— that bare Je - su.

VERSES

1 There is no— rose of such— vir - tue As is the— rose that bare— Je - su.

Al - le - - - luy - - - - - - a.

2   For in this Rose contained was
    Heaven and earth in little space
       Res miranda.

4   The angels sing, the shepherds too,
    Gloria in excelsis Deo'
       Gaudeamus.

3   (And) by that Rose we may well see
    There be one God in Persons three
       Gaudeamus.

5   (Now) leave we all this worldly mirth
    And follow we this joyful birth
       Transeamus.

(1) Two beats' rest omitted at the points marked with an asterisk. *R.R.Terry*
(2) This note stands *Si* in the MS. but the descant shows it to be an obvious miscopy for *La. R.R.Terry*

76. CHESTER CAROL

Qui creavit coelum

Late medieval carol (E.R.)

1 He who made the earth so fair, lul-ly, lul-ly lu,
Slum-bers in a sta-ble bare, by by, by by, by,
Warm'd by cat-tle stand-ing there, lul-ly, lul-ly, lu!

2 Oxen, lowing, stand all round, Lully, lully, lu:
In the stall no other sound, By, by, by, by, by:
Mars the peace by Mary found, Lully, lully, lu.

3 Joseph piles the soft sweet hay, *etc.*
Starlight drives the dark away,
Angels sing a heavenly lay,

4 Jesus sleeps in Mary's arm, *etc.*
Sheltered there from rude alarm,
None can do Him ill or harm,

5 See his Mother O'er Him bend, *etc.*
Hers the joy to soothe and tend,
Hers the bliss that knows no end

Irene Gass

Words and music from the 'Chester Mysteries'
This should always be sung by boys' or women's voices in unison, with a very light and flexible accompaniment.

77. SWEET WAS THE SONG THE VIRGIN SANG

Words and melody from WILLIAM BALLET'S Lute Book
(R.T.)

Mode II

Sweet was the song the vir-gin sang When_ When

When she to Beth-lem Ju - da came And was de - li - ver'd

of a Son The bles - sed Je - sus hath to name.

Lul - la, lul - la, lul - la, lul-la-by, lul - la, lul - la,
lul - la, lul-la-by, lul - la-by__
lul - la - by__

103

78. UPON MY LAP MY SOVREIGN SITS

*MARTIN PEERSON
c.1580-1650/51
(C.F.S.)

2 By Babe, my Bliss, my Child, my Choice.
   My Fruit, my Flower, and Bud,
   My Jesus, and my only Joy,
   The sum of all my good.
       Sing lullaby *etc*.

3 Yet as I am, and as I may,
   I must and will be thine:
   Though all too little for thy selfe,
   Vouchsafing to be mine.
       Sing lullaby *etc*.

Richard Verstegan (Rowlands)(1565-1620)

79. LULLAY MY LIKING

Words from a SLOANE MS.
15th cent.

GUSTAV HOLST

VERSE 3

Solo

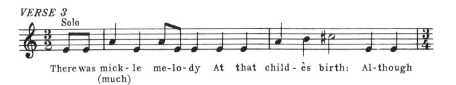

There was mick-le me-lo-dy At that child-ès birth: Al-though
(much)

they were in hea-ven's bliss They ma- dè mick-le mirth: *REFRAIN*

VERSE 4

Full

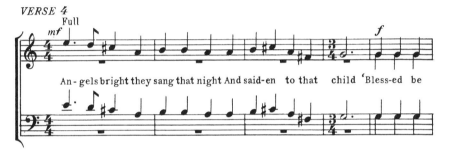

An- gels bright they sang that night And said-en to that child 'Bless-ed be

thou, and so be she that is so meek and mild; *REFRAIN*

VERSE 5

Solo

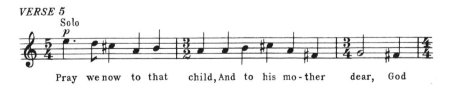

Pray we now to that child, And to his mo- ther dear, God

grant them all his bless- ing That now mak- en cheer: *REFRAIN*

80. ADAM LAY YBOUNDEN

JOHN IRELAND

With easy movement ♩.=60

Ad - am lay y - bound - en, Bound- en in a bond;—

Four— thou-sand win - ter Thought he not too long,— And

all was for an ap-ple, An ap-ple that he took,—

As— clerk-ès find - en writ-ten in their book.—

Ne had the ap - ple tak - en been The ap - ple tak - en been,—

Ne had never our la - dy A - been Hea-ven-è queen.

Bless-èd be the time That ap - ple tak - en was.

There-fore we moun sing - en De - o Grac-i - as!

Bless - èd be the time That ap - ple tak - en was.

There-fore we moun sing - en De - o Grac-i - as!

15th century

81. NEW PRINCE, NEW POMP

JOHN IRELAND
1879-

No - well, — No - well, No - well, — Sing we with mirth! Christ is come well, with us — to dwell, By — his — most no - ble — birth. —

1. Be - hold — a sim - ple ten - der
2. The Inns — are full; no man — will
3. Des - pise — him not for ly — ing
4. Weigh not his crib, his wood - en
5. This sta - ble is a princ - es
6. The per - sons in that poor — at -
7. With gay ap - proach, O Christ - ian

★ The prelude 'Nowell' is an old 'burden' but not by Southwell.

110

babe, In ___ freez - ing wint - er night, In ___
yield This _ lit - tle pil - grim bed; But _
there; First _ what ___ he is ___ en - quire: An ___

dish, Nor beasts that by ___ him feed; Weigh
court, This crib his chair _ of state, The
tire His roy - al liv - ries wear; The
wight, Do hom - age to ___ thy King; And

home - ly mang - er ___ trem - bling lies: A -
forced ___ he is with sim - ple beasts In
Or - ient pearl is ___ oft - en found In

not ___ his moth - er's poor ___ at - tire, Nor
beasts ___ are par - cel of ___ his pomp, The
Prince ___ him - self has come ___ from heav'n. This
high - ly praise this hum - ble pomp, Which

las! ___ a pit - eous ___ sight. ___
crib ___ to shroud his ___ head. ___
depth ___ of dir - ty ___ mire. ___

Jos - eph's sim - ple meed. ___
wood - en dish his plate. ___
pomp ___ is priz - èd there. ___
he ___ from heav'n doth bring. ___

A ballad-setting of these words will be found at No 43.

Robert Southwell

111

E

82. BELL CAROL

ERIC H. THIMAN

dong, Ding dong, Ding dong. Ding dong, Ding dong.

2. The
3. Then

Ding dong, Ding dong. Ding dong, Ding dong.

bells ring out their mes-sage clear That Christ is born, that Son so dear.
Christ-ians join on Christ-mas morn To wor-ship Him, the Babe new-born.

. Glo-ry to God in the high-est. _____ Ding dong, Ding

dong, Ding dong, Ding dong, Ding dong, Ding dong, Ding dong, Ding

dong, Ding dong, Ding dong, Ding dong, Ding dong.

D.S.

Anon.

* A in Soprano for v. 3 only
† pause for v. 3 only

113

83. A CHILDING SLEPT

Eric H Thiman

Andante
(Verses 1, 3 & 5)

p 1. A Child - ing slept with - in ___ a bed, Where

mf 3. And then ___ saw they the won - 'drous star Shine
f 5. From Death he rose and left ___ the grave, And

1. cat - tle stood a - bout ___ his head; And sweet - est Mai - den
3. in the East - ern sky ___ a - far. The Wise Men then their
5. us poor men from Hell ___ did save, The King of Glo - ry

1. o'er ___ him lean'd 'Twas Ma - ry, Vir - gin Mo - ther deem'd.
3. gifts did bring And knelt be - fore their Lit - tle King.
5. He doth stand All by th' Al - migh - ty Fa - ther's hand.

REFRAIN (♩.=♪)
p   *p*

My gracious Lord and King, He was that fair Child - ing.

114

Verses 2 & 4 (Optional)
S.S.A.

mf 2. And An - gel voi - ces sang __ a - round, And
p 4. The man of sor - rows he __ be - came, And

2. Glo - ry and
4. He died and

2. pour - èd forth a heav'n - ly sound; Glo - ry and Hon - our
4. on the cross was known to fame; He died and came to

2. loud __ out - pour __ Be to our God for ev - er - more.
4. bu - ri - al Was lift - ed up, to lift __ us all.

REFRAIN (♪=♪)
p S.A.T.B.

My gra - cious Lord and King, He was that fair Child - ing.

Anon.

115

84. WHEN MARY CAME TO BETHLEHEM

F. E. LIGHT

1. When Ma-ry came to Beth-le-hem At Cæs-ar's high de-cree, Naught
2. Up-on a fra-grant bed of hay And watch'd by si-lent kine, She
3. The ox and ass with gen-tle eyes Be-held their In-fant King, While
4. The dus-ty beams the sha-dow'd walls, Shine in a heav'n-ly glow, The

but a sta - ble could be found Where she might shel-ter'd be. ___
nursed her ba - by in her arms, Her lit - tle Lord Di - vine. __
from the heights an - gel - ic hosts Sped down on shin-ing wing. __
Light of all __ the World is come To live with man be - low. __

REFRAIN

A lit-tle ba-by Boy In a wood-en man-ger laid, ___

Son of God most high, __ Born to Ma-ry, Vir-gin Maid.

W. M. Hogan

85. THE THREE KINGS

PETER CORNELIUS
(E. R.)

117

Note:- Cornelius originally wrote this carol as a song for solo voice and piano accompaniment. It is here so arranged that the solo voice can be accompanied by a four-part choir, without an instrument. The choir may sing either the words here set (very softly except in the last three bars), or to a clear vowel-sound without articulation. But if Cornelius's original conception is wanted, the pianist will achieve it by playing the notes printed in small type instead of the chords given to the choir; in the first half he should add an octave to the bass and fill up the treble chords as may be harmonically suitable.

The chorale sung by the choir is a version of *Wie schön leuchtet der Morgenstern*, by P. Nicolai (d. 1599), with words by Alfred Angel.

E*

86. WATCHING MY SHEEP

Als ich bei meinen Schafen wacht

German Carol
(C. K-S.)

120

N.B. The Altos come down to lower stave here.
Translation of Refrain— 'With a song let us bless the Lord'.

87. THOU MUST LEAVE THY LOWLY DWELLING

HECTOR BERLIOZ
(E.R.)

1 Thou must leave thy low - ly
2 Bles - sed Je - sus we im -
3 Blest are ye be - yond all

dwell-ing, The hum - ble crib, the sta - ble bare.
-plore thee With hum - ble love and ho - ly fear,
mea-sure, Thou hap - py fa - ther, Mo - ther mild.

1 Babe all mor - tal Babes ex - cel-ling

Babe, mor - tal Babes ex - cel-ling, Con - tent _ our
In the land that lies _ be - fore thee, For - get _ not
Guard ye well your heav'n - ly trea-sure, The Prince of

1 Babe _ all _ Babes

earth - ly lot _ to share, Lov - ing fa - ther, lov - ing
us _ who lin - ger here. May the shep herd's low - ly
peace, the ho - ly Child. God go with you, God pro-

mo - ther Shel - ter thee with ten - der care!
call - ing E - ver to thy heart be dear.
-tect you, Guide you safe - ly through the wild!

Lov - ing fa - ther, lov - ing mo - ther Shel - ter
May the shep-herd's low - ly call - ing E - ver
God go with you, God pro - tect you, Guide you

thee with ten - der care: Shel - ter thee with ten - der
to thy heart be dear: E - ver to thy heart be
safe - ly through the wild! Guide you safe - ly through the

1-2   3 ★   (accompaniment)

care.
dear.
      wild.   ppp
                                    Words by Paul England

*hold these bars.

This carol may be sung unaccompanied, but it was, of course, originally conceived with orchestral accompaniment. The accompanying instrument may follow the vocal parts as written here, or if preferred, may be played from the vocal score of the *Childhood of Christ* (Novello's Edition) pp.76-81.

123

88. FANFARE
Gloria in Excelsis Deo

MARTIN SHAW, 1875-1958

*This may be sung twice through, once unacc. (*p*) then accomp. (*ff*).

124

89. ODE ON THE NATIVITY
Rorate Caeli

London

Melody by J. SHEELES 1688-1761
(E.R.)

1 *Ro - ra - te__ cae - li__* de - su - *per!* Hea - vens,__ dis - til your balm - y__show'rs, For__ now__ is__ ris'n the bright day - star From the__ rose Ma - ry,__ flow'r of flow'rs. The__ clear Sun, whom no cloud de - vours, Sur - mount - ing Phoe - bus__ in the East, Is__

126

com - en__ of__ his__ heav'n - ly__tow'rs: *Et* *no - bis__ Pu - er*

na - tus__ est, Et__ no - bis Pu - er__ na - tus__ est.

2   Sinners, be glad and penance do,
       And thank your Maker heartfully;
       For He that ye might not come to
       To you is comen full humbly,
       Your soul-es with his blood to buy,
       And loose you of the fiend's arrest --
       And only of his own mercy:
       Pro nobis Puer natus est.

3   . Now spring up flow-ers from the root,
       Revert you upward nat'rally,
       In honour of this blessed fruit
       That rose up from the rose Mary ;
       Lay out your leav-es lustily,
       From dead take life now at the last,
       In worship of that Prince worthy,
       Qui nobis Puer natus est.

4   Sing, heav'n imperial, most of height!
       Regions of air make harmony !
       All fish in flood and fowl of flight
       Be mirthful and make melody!
       All *'Gloria in excelsis'* cry !
       Heav'n, earth and sea, man, bird and beast --
       He that is crown'd above the sky,
       Pro nobis Puer natus est.

William Dunbar, c. 1465- c. 1520

These four verses are taken from the nine verses of the Ode on the Nativity by Scotland's greatest
poet. The Latin words with which it opens mean 'Drop dew, ye heavens, from above'.-- a reference to Isa.
45.8. The tune was originally written for 'The spacious firmament on high', a hymn by Joseph Addison.
It was first set to these words in the *Westminster Hymnal* (1940 edition).

90. FROM HEAVEN HIGH

Scottish Carol tune
(E.R.)

1 From hea - ven high I come to tell The best no -
2 This day_ to you is born a child of Ma - ry
3 My soul_ and life, stand up_ and see who lies in

4 0 my_ dear heart, young Je - sus sweet, pre - pare thy

- wells that ev-er_ be - fell. To you these ti - dings
meek and Vir - gin mild. That bles - sed bairn_ so
a - né crib_ of tree. What babe is this, _ so

cra - dle in_ my spreit And I_ shall rock_ thee

true_ I bring, and I_ will of_ them say_ and sing.
gen-tle and kind Shall you re - joice_ both heart and mind.
good_ and fair? 'Tis Je - sus Christ, God's son_ and heir.

in_ my heart_ and nev - er more_ from thee_ de - part.

Words modernised (in part) from the Scottish translation of Martin Luther's *Vom Himmel hoch* in *Ane Compendious Booke of Godly and Spiritual Songs* (Edinburgh 1621). The tune is from the same source.

128

91. CHILD IN THE MANGER

Celtic Carol tune
(E. R.)

Leanabh an aigh

1 Child in the manger,
  Infant of Mary;
Outcast and stranger,
  Lord of all!
Child who inherits
  All our transgressions,
All our demerits
  On Him fall.

2 Once the most holy
    Child of salvation,
  Gently and lowly,
    Lived below;
  Now, as our glorious
    Mighty Redeemer,
  See Him victorious
    O'er each foe.

3 Prophets foretold Him,
    Infant of wonder;
  Angels behold Him
    On His throne;
  Worthy our Saviour
    Of all their praises;
  Happy for ever
    Are His own.

Mary Macdonald
Tr. by Lachlan Macbean

129

92. COME YE THANKFUL PEOPLE

Irish Carol tune
(E.R.)

1 Come ye thank-ful peo-ple and wel-come Christ to earth With
2 A maid-en and a ba-by, a sta-ble cold and bare, Yet
3 Ho - ly, Ho - ly, Ho-ly, the glo-rious an - gels cry, And

songs of joy and glad-ness at this a - ma - zing birth. For
nev - er was there pa-lace that could with this com-pare. For
Ho - ly, Ho - ly, Ho-ly, let Chris-tians now re - ply:

now with-in the man-ger the new-born ba - by lies, For
here the Queen of an-gels her son and God a - dores,While
Gold and myrrh and in-cense are gifts from Eas - tern kings, But

him the an-gels mu-sic is ring-ing through the skies. They
he his heav'n-ly Fa-ther for all man - kind im-plores. He
prayer and a - do - ra-tion the poor-est of us brings, As

130

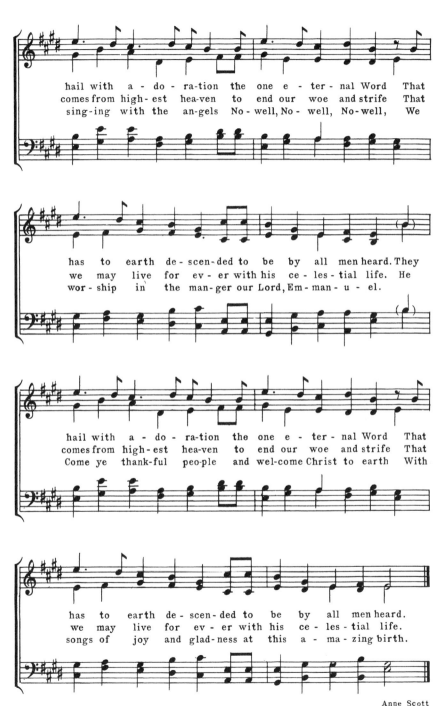

hail with a - do - ra-tion the one e - ter - nal Word That
comes from high - est hea-ven to end our woe and strife That
sing-ing with the an-gels No - well, No - well, No-well, We

has to earth de - scen-ded to be by all men heard. They
we may live for ev - er with his ce - les - tial life. He
wor - ship in the man-ger our Lord, Em-man - u - el.

hail with a - do - ra-tion the one e - ter - nal Word That
comes from high - est hea-ven to end our woe and strife That
Come ye thank-ful peo-ple and wel-come Christ to earth With

has to earth de - scen-ded to be by all men heard.
we may live for ev - er with his ce - les - tial life.
songs of joy and glad-ness at this a - ma - zing birth.

Anne Scott

93. DECK THE HALL

'Nos Galan'

Welsh carol
(E.R.)

1 Deck the hall with boughs of hol-ly,
2 See the blaz-ing yule be-fore us,
3 Fast a-way, the old year pass-es,
Fa la la la la, la la la la,

'Tis the sea-son to be jol-ly,
Strike the harp and join the cho-rus,
Hail the new ye lads and lass-es,
Fa la la la la, la la la la.

Don we now our gay ap-par-ell,
Fol-low me in mer-ry mea-sure,
Sing we joy-ous al-to-ge-ther
Fa la la la, la la la la,

Troll the an-cient yule-tide ca-rol,
While I tell of yule-tide trea-sure,
Heed-less of the wind and wea-ther,
Fa la la la, la la la la.

Traditional

132

94. GREETINGS GOOD MASTER
La Guignolee

Canadian Carol
(E.R.)

1   Greetings, good master, mistress, children,
     Greetings, good health to one and all!
Once more we come to you with singing,
Open your door, we've come to call.
     Let us now to your hearth draw near,
       With warmth and with food let us be welcomed:
Greetings, good master, mistress, children,
     We hope our songs will bring good cheer.
We wish you all a merry Christmas
And a most happy New Year.

2   Greetings, good master, mistress, children,
       If our singing does not please,
We shall not be the least offended,
     Though you now leave us here to freeze.
       Far we have travelled on this day
         To sing and to bring the season's greetings.
Therefore, good master, mistress, children,
     Will you now kindly lend an ear?
Let us wish you a merry Christmas
And a most happy New Year.

Ruth Heller

133

95. 'TWAS IN THE MOON OF WINTER-TIME

'Jesus Anatolia'

Canadian carol
(Originally French)
(E. R.)

1 'Twas in the moon of win-ter-time, When all the birds had fled, That migh-ty Git-chi Ma-ni-tou Sent an-gel-choirs in-stead;___ Be-fore their light the stars grew dim, And won-d'ring hun-ters heard the hymn:

CHORUS

Je-sus your King is born,

Je - sus is born, In ex - cel - sis glo - ri - a.

2 Within a lodge of broken bark
   The tender Babe was found,
   A ragged robe of rabbit skin
   Enwrapped his beauty round:
   But as the hunter braves drew nigh,
   The angel-song rang loud and high.

   Jesus your King is born.

3 The earliest moon of winter-time
   Is not so round and fair
   As was ring of glory on
   The helpless Infant there.
   The chiefs from far before him knelt
   With gifts of fox and beaver-pelt.

   Jesus your King is born.

4 O children of the forest face,
   O sons of Manitou,
   The Holy Child of earth and heaven
   Is born to-day for you.
   Come kneel before the radiant Boy,
   Who brings you beauty, peace, and joy.

   Jesus your King is born.

J. Edgar Middleton

Gitchi-Manitou: Indian expression for the supreme Deity (as in Longfellow's *Hiawatha).*

96. AWAY IN A MANGER

Melody by W.J.Kirkpatrick
(E.R.)

1 A - way in a — man-ger, no — crib for a bed, — The — lit - tle Lord Je - sus laid down His sweet head. The stars in the bright sky looked down where He lay, — The — lit - tle Lord Je - sus a - sleep on the hay.

2 The cattle are lowing, the baby awakes,
  But little Lord Jesus no crying he makes,
  I love Thee, Lord Jesus! Look down from the sky
  And stay by my side until morning is nigh.

3 Be near me, Lord Jesus: I ask Thee to stay,
  Close by me for ever, and love me, I pray,
  Bless all the dear children in Thy tender care
  And fit us for heaven, to live with Thee there.

Anon.

97. AWAY IN A MANGER
(2nd tune)

Basque Carol
(E.P.)

Lightly, moderately quickly

1. A - way in a__ man-ger, no__ crib for a bed, The__
lit - tle Lord Je - sus laid down His sweet head; The stars in the__
bright sky looked down where He lay, The__ lit - tle Lord

Verses 1 and 2
Je - sus a - sleep on the hay.

Verse 3
live with Thee there.

2. The cattle are lowing, the baby awakes;
But little Lord Jesus, no crying He makes:
I love Thee, Lord Jesus; look down from the sky,
And stay by my side until morning is nigh.

3. Be near me, Lord Jesus; I ask Thee to stay
Close by me for ever, and love me, I pray;
Bless all the dear children in Thy tender care,
And fit us for heaven to live with Thee there.

Anonymous

137

98. WE THREE KINGS OF ORIENT ARE

J. H. HOPKINS

1. We three kings of O - rient are; Bear - ing gifts we tra-verse a - far, Field and foun - tain, moor and moun-tain, Fol-low-ing yon - der star.

REFRAIN

O_____ star of won - der, star of night, Star with

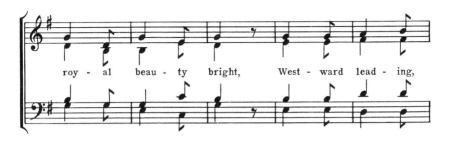

roy - al beau - ty bright, West - ward lead - ing,

D. %

still pro - ceed - ing, Guide us to Thy per - fect light.

Melchior
Born a King on Bethlehem's plain,
Gold I bring, to crown Him again,
King for ever, ceasing never,
Over us all to reign.

Caspar
Frankincense to offer have I,
Incense owns a Deity nigh.
Prayer and praising, all men raising
Worship him, God most high.

Balthazar
Myrrh is mine, its bitter perfume
Breathes a life of gathering gloom;
Sorrowing, sighing, bleeding, dying,
Sealed in the stone-cold tomb.

All
Glorious now behold him arise,
King and God and sacrifice,
Alleluia, Alleluia;
Earth to the heavens replies.

J.H. HOPKINS

99. RISE UP, SHEPHERD, AN' FOLLER

American Spiritual
(E.R.)

There's a star in the east on__ Christ-mas morn,

CHORUS

Rise up, shep-herd, an' fol-ler; It will lead to the place where the

Sa-viour's born, Rise up, shep-herd, an' fol-ler:__

Leave your sheep an' leave your lambs, Rise up, shep-herd, an'

fol-ler;__ Leave your ewes an' leave your rams,

Rise up, shep-herd, an' fol-ler___ Fol - ler, fol - ler,

Rise__ up, shep-herd, an' fol-ler___ Fol -- ler the star of

Beth - le - hem,__ Rise up, shep-herd, an' fol-ler.___

2   If you take good heed of the angel's words,
        Rise up, shepherd, an' foller,
    You'll forget your flocks, you'll forget your herds,
        Rise up, shepherd, an' foller.
    Leave your sheep an' leave your lambs,
        Rise up, shepherd, an' foller,
    Leave your ewes an' leave your rams,
        Rise up, shepherd, an' foller,
            Foller, foller,
        Rise up, shepherd, an' foller,
    Foller the star of Bethlehem,
        Rise up, shepherd, an' foller.

                                Traditional

141

100. CAROL OF THE BIRDS

Australian Carol
WILLIAM G. JAMES

VERSE 2 (Solo or Unison)

Down where the tree-ferns grow by the river,
There where the waters sparkle and quiver,
Deep in the gullies Bell-birds are chiming,
Softly and sweetly their lyric notes rhyming-
"Orana! Orana! To Christmas Day."

VERSE 3 (Full)

Friar-birds sip the nectar of flowers,
Currawongs chant in wattle-tree bowers;
In the blue ranges Lorikeets calling—
Carols of bushbirds rising and falling—
"Orana! Orana! To Christmas Day."

John Wheeler

*Also known as Australian Crane   †"Orana"—Aboriginal word meaning "Welcome"

101. THE THREE DROVERS

Australian Carol
WILLIAM G. JAMES

Gaily – with spirit

mf 1 A-cross the plains — one Christ-mas night, Three dro-vers rid-ing blythe — and gay, — Looked up and saw a star-ry light, More ra-diant than the Mil-ky Way; And on their hearts such won-der fell, they sang with joy "No - el! — No-el! — No-el! No - el! — No-el! — No - el!"

2 The air was dry with Summer heat, and smoke was on the yellow Moon;
   But from the Heavens, faint and sweet, came floating down a wond'rous tune,
   And, as they heard, they sang full well, those drovers three—"Noel! Noel!"

3 The black swans flew across the sky, the wild dog called across the plain,
   The starry lustre blazed on high, still echoed on the Heavenly strain;
   And still they sang "Noel! Noel!" those drovers three. "Noel! Noel!"

John Wheeler

One or more of the verses may be sung in unison, if desired.

F

102. COME, GOOD PEOPLE, LET US SING

Old Flemish Carol
(F.W.S. and G.G.)

Carmel Mount'

Andantino

1. Come, good peo-ple, let us sing Un-to Christ, our new-born King, *Christ-us Na-tus Hod-ie.* Kings and Peoples come to a-dore, Christ,our King for ev-er-more. *Ex Ma-ri-a Vir-gin-e, Ex Ma-ri-a Vir-gin-e.*

2. Come, good christians join the song,
Of that heavenly, happy throng,
   Christus Natus Hodie,
Peace and joy are come to earth,
By the Holy Infant's birth;
   Ex Maria Virgine. (repeat)

3. Let the heavens and earth rejoice,
Sing aloud with cheerful voice,
   Christus Natus Hodie,
Loud sing, then, with holy joy,
For this child, this holy boy,
   Ex Maria Virgine. (repeat)

G. Grimes

This tune is the origin of the theme used by Handel in the Variations of his Suite in E, which later came to be known as 'The Harmonious Blacksmith'. That name, however, has nothing to do with the original tune, being devised from the percussive effect of Handel's first variation.

144

103. MARY AND ST. JOSEPH WENT

French
(G.H.)

1 Ma - ry and Saint Jo - seph went— Je - sus in her arms con -
2 Night was fast suc - ceed - ing day— When a shep-herd came their

- tent— Seek - ing shel - ter of their kind,— But no
way. (*Shepherd*)"Tell me, sir," the shep - herd said,— "Why you

inn a - las could find, But no Inn a - las could find.
walk with wea - ry tread? Why you walk with wea - ry tread?"

(*St. Jos.*) 3 "Shepherd shelter do I seek
     For this Child and Maiden weak."
(*Shep.*) "Sir, your search is at an end,
     This my byre I freely lend."

4 "Take my lamp and cloak withal,
  Enter now within the stall.
  Here the Child and Mother may
  Rest upon this fragrant hay."

(*St. Jos.*) 5 "For your kindness done this day,
     You shall be renowned alway.
     Know the Babe within your stall
     Is a Shepherd to us all."

6 "Down from heaven He comes to keep
  Watch o'er souls which are His sheep.
  So may you in time behold
  Heaven's fields from out His fold."

Pr. G. Grimes

104. NOEL, NOEL, NOEL

(Noel Nouvelet)
(E. R.)

With energy but without haste

1 No - el, No - el, No - el,— Now to - geth - er sing!

Faith - ful peo - ple cry - ing.— 'Lord, our thanks we bring'

Sing - ing No - el, To Him our lit - tle King,—

REFRAIN

No - el, No - el, No - el,— Let your voi - ces ring.

2 Clearly spake the Angel:
'Shepherds, come away!
Peaceful and rejoicing
Bethlem seek this day!
This little Lamb is born to be our King!'
Noel, Noel, Noel,
Let your voices ring.

3 There they found together
Joseph - Mary blest —
Cradling from the weather
Jesus at Her breast!
Only a manger for the Heavenly King!
Noel, Noel, Noel,
Let your voices ring.

4 Kings draw nigh to greet Him,
Neath the shining star,
Seeking Bethlem city
From their countries far.
Here, in the dawn they find their Infant King!
Noel, Noel, Noel,
Let your voices ring.

5 See! one beareth incense,
Others, gold and myrrh!
Offering them to Jesus
Sleeping sweetly there.
See! in the manger, beauty blossoming!
Noel, Noel, Noel,
Let your voices ring.

6 See our Saviour Jesus
Who, by His great deeds
From despair will save us,
Dying for our needs.
Shedding His blood, that all the world may sing,
Noel, Noel, Noel,
Let your voices ring.

Tr. K.W. Simpson
Alt. G.H.

105. BLESSED BE THAT MAID MARIE

Melody from WILLIAM BALLET'S Lute Book
(C.W.)

1 Bles-sed be that Maid Ma - rie; __ Born He was of her bo - dy; __

Ve - ry God ere time be-gan, __ Born in time the Son of Man.

E - ya! Ihe-sus ho - di - e __ Na - tus est de Vir - gi - ne. __

2 In a manger of an ass
   Jesu lay and lullèd was;
   Born to die upon the Tree
   Pro peccante homine.
   Eya! etc.

4 Fare three Kings from far-off land,
   Incense, gold and myrrh in hand;
   In Bethlem the Babe they see,
   Stellæ ducti lumine.
   Eya! etc.

3 Sweet and blissful was the song
   Chanted of the Angel throng,
   "Peace on earth", Alléluya.
   In excelsis gloria.
   Eya! etc.

5 Make we merry on this fest,
   In quo Christus natus est;
   On this Child I pray you call
   To assoil and save us all
   Eya! etc.

   Old English Carol

Latin translations—(v.1) Jesus is born today of the Virgin (v.2) For sinful man (v.3) Glory in the
highest (v.4) Led by the light of a star (v.5) On which Christ was born.   In v. 5 'assoil' =
'procure our forgiveness'.
Although the tune above comes from an English source, it is almost certainly derived from a French
tune, 'Promptement levez-vous mon voisin'. See *O.B.C.* 166 and *E.C.*

148

106. PATAPAN
Guillo, pran ton Tamborin

Old Burgundy Noël
Air: *Ma mere mariez-moi*

Lightly

1. Take thy ta-bor and thy flute, None to-day must
2. Long a-go our fa-thers sang Such a song on
3. As we join our choi-cest airs, In a hymn that

1. e'er be mute: With such jol-ly shep-herd
2. this same day: 'Twas of Beth-le-hem, their
3. up-ward fares: Earth and heav'n seem near our

Tur-e-lur-e-lu, pa-ta-pa-ta-pan;

1. toys, To the
2. lay, Tur-e-lu, pa-ta-pan; Where wise
3. prayers: Van-ish

1. sound of this shrill noise, Let us raise a — No-ël, Boys!
2. Kings and Shepherds stray: To the stars their mu-sic rang.
3. all our dai-ly cares While we dance and sing No-ël.

149

107. SHEPHERDS, REJOICE

French Carol tune
(E.R.)

1 Shep-herds, re - joice,— your Sa-viour is nigh
2 Ma - ry her love - ly babe lays to rest
3 Joy-ful as all— now home-wards de - part

Sing o'er his cra - dle your sweet lul - la - by:
Fold - ing his ten - der limbs close to her breast:
Che - rish this scene of Christ's love in your heart:

Lul - la - by, lul - la - by lul - la - by sing
lul - - - - - - -la - by

Low in his cra - dle lies— Je - sus your King.

Anon.

108. ENTRE LE BOEUF ET L'ANE GRIS

French Carol tune
(E.R.)

1 En - tre le boeuf et ___ l'â - ne gris,
2 En - tre les deux bras de Ma - ri - e,
3 En ce beau jour si ___ so - len - nel,

dort, dort, dort le pe-tit fils; __ Mille an-ges di-vins, __

mil-le sé-ra-phins __ vo-lent à l'en-tour de ce Dieu d'a-mour.

An English Carol on the same theme

1. Now between the ox and ass,
   Fast, fast, sleeps the little Son:
   Hosts of heaven bright
   Hover in the night
   O'er the place where Life lies anew begun.

2. Safely in His mother's arms,
   Fast, fast, sleeps the little Son:
   Now in lullabies
   Mary magnifies
   God as Man for man to the earth come down.

3. While the shepherds leave their sheep
   Fast, fast, sleeps the little Son:
   Do not be afraid!
   See in manger laid,
   Christ the long-expected, the Holy One.

4. Now let every heart rejoice!
   Fast, fast, sleeps the little Son:
   None can take away
   Jesus born today,
   None can e'er undo what His love has done.

T. C. Micklem

F*

109. WHEREFORE THIS GREAT JOY

An old French Air
(E. P.)

Brightly

1. Where-fore this great joy and sing-ing? Why these songs of Ho-ly mirth?
An-gel-choirs from heaven are bring-ing Tid-ings of a Saviour's birth.
Glo - - - ri - a, Glo - ri-a in ex-cel-sis De - o.
Glo-ri - a, Glo-ri-a,
Glo - - - ri - a, Glo - ri-a in ex-cel-sis De - o.

2. Once He came that He might save us
   From the deadly power of sin:
   And, by gifts that once He gave us,
   Peace and love our joy to win.
   Gloria in excelsis, etc.

3. Sing the joy that heaven unfoldeth
   To the hearts that Him adore;
   He, the Saviour earth beholdeth,
   Oh! for grace to love Him more.
   Gloria in excelsis, etc.

4. Year by year the song of glory,
   Doth our hearts and souls inspire;
   As we hear the angel-story,
   In the singing of the choir.
   Gloria in excelsis, etc.

5. Come then, let us now adore Him,
   Bid the heavenly anthems flow;
   Come with praises stand before Him
   And your thankfulness forth shew.
   Gloria in excelsis, etc.

6. To the Holy Babe, Lord Jesus,
   Endless glory ever be,
   To the Father and the Spirit,
   Now and through eternity.
   Gloria in excelsis, etc.
   An old Cornish carol, revised and partly re-written by C.F.

110. COME WITH HEARTS AFIRE

Nous allons, ma mie

French Noël
(R.T.)

1 Come, with hearts a - fire And seek Him where He lies!
2 Tid - ings glad and mirth - ful Fall up - on mine ear!
3 See the o - pen Man - ger! Thronged with rich and poor—

'Tis our dear Mes - si - ah Sent us from the skies!
To His ser - vants faith - ful Soon He will ap - pear!
None to Him a stran - ger, Wide the o - pen door!

Kneel - ing there be - fore Him, Ma - ry, Jo - seph see!
We shall see the Mas - ter Pro - mised now so long,
Fear - less they a - dore Him, (Born a King this day,)

Come now and a - dore Him! Son of God is He!
Hur - ry, Bro - thers fas - ter! Run with joy - ous song!
Lay their Gifts be - fore Him: Come, O come a - way!

Tr. by K. W. Simpson

153

111. I, THE ANGEL AM OF GOD
Je suis L'Archange de Dieu

Words and melody from *Les Noëls Bressans*
(R.T.)

1 I, the An-gel am of God! (O sim-ple peo-ple
In this place ye oft have trod Your mu-sic now a-

heark - en!) Christ is born on earth this day!
- wa - ken!

CHORUS

Lift your voi - ces! Tune your lay! He is come, come, come! See Him

lie, lie, lie! He is come! See Him lie! O so
La La

come-ly, Bro - thers! Fair - er than all o - thers.

In the choruses the translator has imitated the childlike puns of the original.

154

2. Shepherds lift your pipes and play!
   Leave your crooks, uncaring!
   Raise your voices, cry: 'NOE!'*
   All our gladness sharing.
        Cry together now: 'NOE!
        Christ is born this happy day!'
   Cold and bare, bare, bare,
        He doth lie, lie, lie!
   Cold and bare,
        He doth lie!
   Cold, and *barely* clothed,
   Mary's Son beloved!

3. Shepherds gladly look around
   See the Angels winging!
   Join the happy, jocund sound,
   Sing as they are singing!
        Shepherds, now the Babe adore,
        Earth of joy could hold no more!
   To the stall, stall, stall,
        Run ye all, all, all!
   To the stall,
        Run ye all!
   Other hearts *forestalling*,
   *'NOE! NOE!' calling!

4. Leave your flocks, my brothers all,
   Sing in happy chorus!
   Jesus in that quiet stall
   Soon will be before us!
        Come and see, with eyes of faith,
        Jesus now is born on earth!
   That ye may, may, may,
        Sing in joy, joy, joy!
   That ye may,
        Sing in joy,
   That *amazing* wonder
   In the manger yonder!

5. Shepherds tho' He be so poor,
   Lying there so lowly,
   Ye may happily adore
   Christ is here before ye!
        He is Prince of all the skies!
        Majesty within Him lies!
   Born as King, King, King,
        See Him here, here, here!
   Born as King,
        See Him here!
   And, in *asking* of Him,
   We but prove we love Him!

*Pronounced *No-ay*   tr. K.W. Simpson

155

112. THIS NEW CHRISTMAS CAROL

Me anvez eur goulmik

Breton Dance
altered by R.T.

1 This new Christ-mas___ ca - rol Let us cheer-ful-ly

2 Let us all draw___ near Him Both the young and the
3 When the wise men dis - cov-ered The bright hea-ven-ly
4 Now the proud may come hith - er And may per-fect-ly
5 Let us learn of those sa - ges Who were mine to o -

sing, To the hon-our and___ glo-ry of our hea-ven-ly___

old While God's won - drous___ mes-sage in this tale___ is___
star, Then with gold and rich___ spi-ces straight they came from a -
see, The most ex - cel-lent___ pat-tern of hu - ma - ni -
- bey, Nay, we find thro' all___ a - ges they have hon-oured this___

King who was born of a Vir-gin, bles-sed Ma-ry by___

told: How the in-fant King of Hea-ven At his mo - ther's___
- far, In o - be - di-ence to wor-ship With a hea-ven-ly___
- ty; For in - stead of a cra-dle Deck'd with or - na-ments___
day, Ev - er since our re - deem-er's Blest na - ti - vi -

name, For poor sin-ner's re - demp-tion to the world he___ came.

breast Came to___ bring us all glad___ tid-ings In a world op - prest.
mind, Know-ing he, was to us___ born, For the good of man - kind.
gay, Here the heav'n-ly King of___ glo-ry In a man - ger lay.
- ty, Who was born of a___ Vir-gin to set sin - ners___ free.

This old French fragment (consisting of four repetitions of the first phrase) was rewritten by Terry in his edition of *Gilbert and Sandys Carols*.

113. WHAT IS THIS FRAGRANCE?

Quelle est cette odeur agréable?

French Noël (Lorrain)

(R.T.)

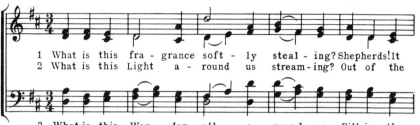

1 What is this fra - grance soft - ly steal - ing? Shepherds! It
2 What is this Light a - round us stream - ing? Out of the

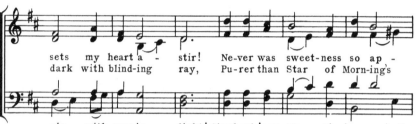

3 What is this Won - der all a - round us Fill-ing the
4 Be not a - fraid, O, Shep - herds low - ly! Hear-ye the
5 There, in a Man - ger with His Mo - ther, Li - eth our

sets my heart a - stir! Ne-ver was sweet-ness so ap -
dark with blind-ing ray, Pu-rer than Star of Morn-ing's

air with mus-ic light! Shepherds! some Ma - gic here hath
An - gel of the Lord! Bear-ing a Mes - sage glad and
Sa - viour, Born to - day! Come a-way Shep-herds; Let none

- peal - ing Ne-ver were flow'rs of spring so fair! — } What is this
seem - ing Showing our path as plain as day! — }

found us! Ne-ver mine ears knew such de - light!
Ho - ly Shedding a rad - iance all a - broad!
oth - er Hin-der thy com - ing now, a - way!

fra-grance soft - ly steal-ing? Shepherds! It sets my heart a - stir.

tr. K. W. Simpson

157

114. QUITTEZ, PASTEURS

French Noel (Besançon melody)
(R. T.)

1 O shep-herds, leave your peace-ful flocks a-graz-ing! No
2 There, low-ly laid, With-in a Man-ger nar-row, A

3 Kings from the East! His Star will guide thee tru-ly! Where
4 Spi-rit Di-vine (Who canst do all things sure-ly), Our

long-er grieve But come, O come a-way! __ Come and a-
love-ly Maid And In-fant thou shalt see! __ His ten-der __

He doth rest In love and faith draw near: __ Our Ris-ing __
hearts en-shrine Thine ar-dours sweet and fair! __ For peace is __

-dore; (Your tears all changed to prais-ing) Of Him the heav'n-ly King __ O
love Hath sought thee in thy sor-row Thy dark-ness to re-move! He

Sun __ Re-ceives thy hom-age du-ly! O bring to Him each one __ Each
his __ That through Thee liv-eth pure-ly! And, ad-ded un-to this __ All

sing, (O sing,) O sing, (O sing) Your Sa-viour born this hap-py day.
came, (He came) to prove, (to prove) A lov-ing Shep-herd's care for thee!

one (Each one!) Each one! (Each one!) Your in-cense and your gold and myrrh!
joy (All joy) and bliss, (and bliss) Since God hath sent His Sa-viour here!

tr. K.W. Simpson

115. SHEPHERDS! SHAKE OFF YOUR DROWSY SLEEP

Chantans! Bargies, Nové, Nové

Besançon Carol
(J.S.)

Brightly
mf

1. Shep-herds! shake off your drow-sy sleep, Rise and
2. Hark! e-ven now the bells ring round, Lis-ten
3. See how the flow'rs all burst a-new, Think-ing
4. Com-eth at length the age of peace, Strife and
5. Shep-herds! then up and quick a-way, Seek the

leave your sil-ly sheep; An-gels from heav'n a-round loud

2. to their mer-ry sound; Hark! how the birds new songs are
3. snow is sum-mer dew; See how the stars a-fresh are
4. sor-row now shall cease; Pro-phets fore-told the won-drous
5. Babe ere break of day; He is the hope of ev-ry

CHORUS
ff

sing-ing, Ti-dings of great joy are bring-ing. Shep-herds! the

2. ma-king As if win-ter's chains were break-ing.
3. glow-ing, All their bright-est beams be-stow-ing. } Shep-herds! the
4. sto-ry Of this Heav'n-born Prince of Glo-ry.
5. na-tion, All in Him shall find sal-va-tion.

poco rit.

cho-rus come and swell! Sing No-el, oh sing No-el!

cho-rus come and swell! Sing No-el, oh sing No-el!

Anon

159

116. DANS CETTE ETABLE

French Carol
Arr. C. GOUNOD

1 Dans cette é - ta - ble Que Jé - sus est char -
1 Je - sus in Sta - ble! What mu - sic may pro -

- mant, Qu'il est ai - ma - ble Dans cet a - bais - se - ment! _ Que
-fess How a - mi - a - ble How lost in low - li - ness? _ All

d'at - traits á la fois! _ Tous les pa - lais des
win - some - ness in small, _ And not a pal - ace -

rois _ N'ont rien de com - pa - ra - ble Aux
- hall _ Has beau - ties com - pa - ra - ble With

char - mes que je vois Dans cette é - ta - - ble!
a - ny that be - fall In yon - der sta - - ble.

2 Que sa puissance
   Paraît bien en ce jour,
   Malgré l'enfance
   Où l'a réduit l'amour!
   Notre ennemi dompté,
   L'enfer déconcerté,
   Font voir qu'en sa naissance
   Rien n'est si redouté
   Que sa puissance.

2 How well His power
   Is manifest this morn
   Though but an hour
   Is gone since he was born!
   Go free the captive may
   And Hell is brought to bay,
   O ere the snowdrop flower
   As manifest as day
   Appears His power.

3 Sans le connaître,
   Dans sa divinité
   Je vois paraître
   Toute sa majesté;
   Dans cet enfant qui naît,
   A son aspect qui plaît,
   Je découvre mon maître,
   Et je sens ce qu'il est
   Sans le connaître.

3 If He has feeling
   'Tis all for our distress,
   The cold congealing
   Makes not his heaviness.
   His favours o'er and o'er
   Invite that all our store
   To Love so self-revealing
   We yield for ever more,
   If we have feeling.

4 Plus de misère!
   Un Dieu souffre pour nous
   Et de son père
   Appaise le courroux;
   C'est en notre faveur
   Qu'il naît dans la douleur;
   Pouvait-il pour nous plaire,
   Unir à sa grandeur
   Plus de misère.

4 Oh! happy wonder!
   Christ Jesus by His pain
   Dissolves the thunder
   Of wrath to sunlit rain.
   To save the sinful soul
   He comes in utter dole
   And Majesty goes under
   To love beyond control,
   Oh! happy wonder!

J.O'Connor

161

117. GOD IN HIGHEST HEAVEN

Jésus Christ s'habille en pauvre

Picardy Carol
(E.R.)

f 1 God in high-est hea - ven___ see - ing all man's bit-ter
mf 2 God the Son the Word e - ter - nal made him-self a

grief and___ shame___ Laid a - side his pow'r, his
man on___ earth,___ En - ter - ing a world that

ma-jes-ty, his bliss, To the res-cue swift - ly___ came.
he him-self had made Through the low-ly gate of___ birth.

mp 3 There the baby lay in a manger
For his mother had no bed,
Thirty years went by, and still the Son of God
Had no place to lay his head.

p 4 Yet he did not rest till, testing
Every depth of utter loss,
He, the Lord, was hanging, nailed through hands and feet,
Stripped·and dead upon a cross.

f 5 Jesus, Master, King of glory,
Teach us loving you alone,
With a joyous will to follow you in peace
By the road that you have shown.

Anne Scott

The association of this tune with a solemn eucharistic hymn in English hymn books should, not pre-
judice its interpretation here: it is a French peasant carol and should be sung simply and more or
less in speech rhythm.

118. CHRIST IS BORN IN BETHLEHEM

Catalan Carol
arranged T. A.

1 Christ is born in Bethlehem
In a stable lowly :
Ox and ass are watching there
O'er the infant Holy :
He is God, though weak and small
He is King and Lord of all.
Let the church-bells ring
As the angels sing
Ding-a-dong .
Bring a song :
Come and kneel before Him
Ever to adore Him.

2 Monarchs bring from countries far
Gifts for His adorning,
They were guided by a star ;
Angels gave them warning.
Gifts of frankincense and gold,
Myrrh for suff'ring that's foretold,
And the church-bells ring
As the angels sing
Ding-a-dong,
Bring a song :
As we kneel before Him
Ever to adore Him.

3 Holy Child of Bethlehem
Grant us now a blessing,
Bring us all to be with Thee
Thy true peace possessing.
Keep us ever in Thy grace:
May we see Thee face to face
Where the angels sing
To the heavenly King,
And the song
Echoes long
To the throne ascending—
Joy that's never ending .

Paraphrase by Thomas Armstrong

119. THE JOYS OF CHRISTMAS

Smoothly and brightly
Unison or Solo

Basque Festival Song (E. P.)

1. Joy is come from God a - bove To all those who Christ-mas love,

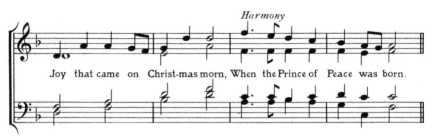

Harmony

Joy that came on Christ-mas morn, When the Prince of Peace was born.

Unison ($\bullet$ = 76)

Sing we mer - ri - ly, sing No - well, Sing the babe, Em - man - u - el.

2. Peace is come from God above
To all those who Christmas love,
Peace we may not understand
In a weary strife-worn land.
Sing we merrily, *etc.*

3. Grace is come from God above
To all those who Christmas love,
Celebrating Jesu's birth.
Singing songs with Holy mirth.
Sing we merrily, *etc.*

4. Love is come from God above
To all those who Christmas love,
Love that casteth fear away,
For God's love is born this day.
Sing we merrily, *etc.*

5. Faith is come from God above
To all those who Christmas love,
Faith that giveth sight to see
All this wondrous mystery.
Sing we merrily, *etc.*

6. Hope is come from God above
To all those who Christmas love,
Hope, new-born on this glad day,
God shall wipe all tears away.
Sing we merrily, *etc.*

7. Of this wondrous birth then sing
Songs of joy with carolling,
Evermore our song shall be,
Hail our Lord's Nativity.
Sing we merrily, *etc.*

E. Pettman

164

120. LOVELY BABY, MARY BORE HIM
Aur txiki

Old Basque Carol
(R.T.)

1 Love - ly Ba - by; Ma - ry bore Him— All make—
2 Ev - 'ry - bo - dy runs to meet Him— All our—
3 Hap - py mor - tals who be - hold Him;— Hap - pi -

haste to kneel be - fore Him; Let us go now and a -
ea - ger - ness to greet Him; An - gels are sing - ing so
- er the arms en - fold Him; Hard on the door of the

- dore Him. O - pen quick - ly; let us in.—
sweet - ly: Glo - ry be to God on high.—
sta - ble, Hard we knock a doz - en times.—

Je - sus, Ma - ry, Hail!— Je - sus, Jo - seph, Hail!

Tr. John Gray

165

121. THE INFANT KING
Oi! Betleem!

Basque Noël (E. P.)

Smoothly, and not too fast

1. Sing lul-la - by! Lul-la-by ba - by, now re - clin - ing, Sing lul-la-
- by! Hush, do not wake the In - fant King. An-gels are watching, stars are
shin-ing O-ver the place where He is ly - ing: Sing lul-la - by!
pp Sing— lul-la - by! Sing lul-la - by!

2.   Sing lullaby!
Lullaby baby, now a-sleeping,
Sing lullaby!
Hush, do not wake the Infant King,
Soon will come sorrow with the morning,
Soon will come bitter grief and weeping:
Sing lullaby!

3.   Sing lullaby!
Lullaby baby, now a-dozing,
Sing lullaby!
Hush, do not wake the Infant King,
Soon comes the cross, the nails, the piercing,
Then in the grave at last reposing
Sing lullaby!

4.   Sing lullaby!
Lullaby! is the babe a-waking?
Sing lullaby!
Hush, do not stir the Infant King.
Dreaming of Easter, gladsome morning,
Conquering Death, its bondage breaking:
Sing lullaby!

S. Baring-Gould

122. I SAW A MAIDEN

An old Basque Noël
with Refrain added by E.P.

1. I saw a maid-en sit-ting and sing, She lull'd her child a lit-tle Lord-ing. Lul-lay,___ Lul-lay,___ my dear son, my sweet-ing. Lul-lay,___ Lul-lay,___ My___ dear son, my___ own dear dear___ ing.

2. This very Lord, He made all things,
   And this very God, the King of all Kings.
   Lullay, etc.

3. There was sweet music at this Child's birth,
   And Heaven filled with angels, making much mirth.
   Lullay, etc.

4. Heaven's Angels sang to welcome the Child
   Now born of a maid, all undefiled.
   Lullay, etc.

5. Pray we and sing on this Festal day,
   That Peace may dwell with us alway.
   Lullay, etc.

16th century English

123. BETHLEHEM'S STALL

Abets zagun guziek

Old Basque carol
(R.T.)

1 Beth - le - hem's dark - en'd ci - ty
2 Seek - ing the shed be - fore _____ them, _____
3 Saw they His glo - ry, shed - ding. _____

Ma - ry and Jo - seph sought,

Turn - ing, with hearts ___ for - lorn,
Ra - di - ance o'er _____ them all:

Ask - ing (for love or pi - ty) _____

There with the cat - tle o'er _____ Him _____
Light - ing His mea - gre bed - ding, _____

Ha - ven for hearts ___ dis - traught;

Je - sus their Son _____ was born.
Gild - ing His lone - ly stall:

168

Houses were shut _____ up - on _____ them; _____
Yet, did the Prin - ces seek Him, _____
'NO - EL! GLAD NO - EL!' cry - ing _____

Faces were cold _____ and stark; _____
Shep-herds and Ma - gi wise, _____
Wor - ship - ping at _____ His feet; _____

Fire there was none _____ to warm _____ them;
Kings rode in haste _____ to greet _____ Him,
Faith (like our own) _____ un - dy - ing,

Can - dle to light the dark.
light _____ the dark.
Un - der the star - ry skies.
star - ry skies.
Blend-ing their ac - cents sweet.
ac - cents sweet.

169   K.W. Simpson

124. LEAD ME TO THY PEACEFUL MANGER
Ez dukezu

Basque carol melody
(collected by FR. DONOSTIA)
(R. T.)

1 Lead me to Thy peace-ful man - ger, Won-'drous

2 Let me lis - ten to the sto - ry, Full of
3 Bless-ed Je - sus, ho - ly Sa - viour, Off-spring

Babe of Beth - le - hem ; Shep - herds

all sur - pass - ing love, How the
of the roy - al Maid, By Thy

hail Thee yet a stran - ger ; Let me

Lord of grace and glo - ry Left for
meek and pure be - ha - viour In her

For Matthew Bridges' original lines see his collected poems. (R. T.)

wor - ship Thee with them.   I am
us   His   throne a - bove: Tou h'd with
fold - ing arms dis - play'd;   F y Thy

vile, but Thou art ho - ly; Oh, u - nite__ my poor heart to
sym - pa - thy so ten - der, Man a - do - reth while se - raphs
tears of earl-iest an - gu¦sh, On Thy sweet in - fant brow im-

Thee;_____ Make me con - trite, keep me
gaze_____ And with glad - ness we sur-
pearl'd,_____ By the love__ that could not

low - ly, Pure as Thou__ would'st have me be.
ren - der Soul and bo - dy__ to Thy praise.
lan - guish Thou hast saved a __ ruin'd world.

Matthew Bridges

171

125. WHO WERE THE SHEPHERDS?

Etzen bada Marie?

Basque carol
(R.T.)

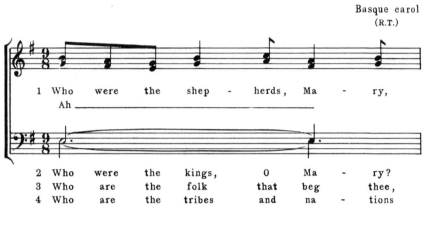

1 Who were the shep - herds, Ma - ry,
Ah ____

2 Who were the kings, O Ma - ry?
3 Who are the folk that beg thee,
4 Who are the tribes and na - tions

Hast-en-ing to a-dore Je-sus the ten - der Ba - by

Tell us if that be true: Kings on a jour - ney, seek - ing
Crowd-ing a - bout thy feet: Af-ter our ex - ile show__ us
Clad in their robes and crowned, Strik-ing their harps and sing - ing

No - one had seen ____ be - fore?

Je - sus they strange - ly knew.
Je - sus thy Babe ____ most sweet?
Hymns of so sweet ____ a sound?

Yes, they were sim - ple shep - herds,
Kings from a dis - tant coun - try,
Those are the mil - lions He ran - soms,
Those are the hosts un - num - be - red,

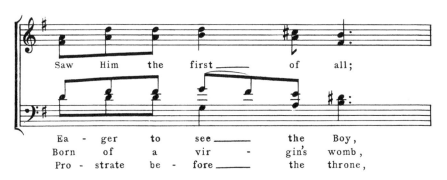

Saw Him the first ___ of all;
Ea - ger to see ___ the Boy,
Born of a vir - gin's womb,
Pro - strate be - fore ___ the throne,

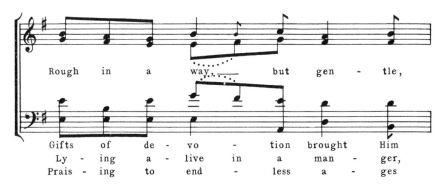

Rough in a way, ___ but gen - tle,
Gifts of de - vo - tion brought Him
Ly - ing a - live in a man - ger,
Prais - ing to end - less a - ges

Lov - ing and pi - ti - ful.
Fill - ing His heart ___ with joy.
Dead and di - vine in a tomb.
Him who is Lord ___ a - lone.

tr. John Gray

173

126. TO BETHLEHEM

Eguberriren jitiaz

Basque Noël
(E. P.)

1. Joseph and gentle Mary came Unto the town of Bethlehem, Weary of foot, and faint for bread, Knowing not where to lay the head. Sing Hallelujah! sing Noël! — Sing we right lustily and well; Jesus is born, the angels tell — Sing we right lustily Noël!

2. Night-dews fell heavy, way was far,
Twinkled aloft one frosty star;
Out of the tavern loud resound
Shouting of men and barking of hound.
Sing Hallelujah! etc.

3. Revellers, royst'rers, welcome they,
Travelling lowly—can they pay?
Not to the needy opens the door:
Out in the cold must lodge the poor.
Sing Hallelujah! etc.

4. So, in a cave where oxen house,
Where the poor cattle all must browse,
There must the mother lay her Child—
Lo, this thy shelter, Mary mild!
Sing Hallelujah! etc.

5. Here upon Christmas no welcome find,
Here not a home, no bidding kind,
Yet out of heav'n the angels sing,
"Glory to God—is born the King!"
Sing Hallelujah! etc.

S. Baring-Gould

127. UNTO US A CHILD IS BORN

German Carol
(E.R.)

1 Un-to us a child is born, To us a son is giv-en, Won-der-ful and Coun-sel-lor, The migh-ty Lord of hea-ven, The migh-ty Lord of hea-ven.

2   Cradled in a stall was he
     Where cattle fed around him,
     There the wise men from afar
     A-seeking came and found him.

3   Herod king was sore afraid
     When he heard this telling,
     'Slay' said he, 'all babes this night,
     Who in my realm are dwelling'.

4   Then to Egypt Joseph went,
     By angel vision bidden,
     There with Mary to abide,
     The child from danger hidden.

5   Of his mercy and his grace
     We now tell out the story,
     How there came from heaven above
     For us the King of glory

Cyril Brenchley

The melody is here given in a form nearer to the original than that, from *Piae Cantiones* (1582) which is normally sung. Edgar Pettman came to this conclusion after examining several MSS earlier in date than 1582.

G

128. CHRIST WAS BORN ON CHRISTMAS DAY

Resonet in Laudibus

Melody from Piae Cantiones (1582)
(E.R.)

Unison

(Women) 1 Christ was born on Christ-mas day; Wrathe the hol-ly
(Men) 2 He is born to set us free, He is born our
(Women) 3 Let the bright red ber-ries glow Ev-'ry-where in
(Men) 4 Chris-tian men, re-joice and sing; 'Tis the birth-day

Harmony

twine the bay; *Chris - tus na - tus ho - di - e:* The
Lord to be, *Ex Ma - ri - a vir - gi - ne:* The
good - ly show; *Chris - tus na - tus ho - di - e:* The
of the King, *Ex Ma - ri - a vir - gi - ne:* The

Babe, the Son the Ho - ly one of Ma - ry.
God, the Lord, by all a - dored for ev - er.
Babe, the Son the Ho - ly one of Ma - ry.
God, the Lord, by all a - dored for ev - er.

5 Night of sad - ness: morn of glad - ness ev - er-more:

Ev - er, Ev - er, Af - ter ma - ny

trou-bles sore, Morn of glad-ness ev - er-more and ev - er-more.

6 Mid-night scarce-ly pass'd and o - ver, Draw-ing to this

repeat **pp**

ho - ly morn: ve - ry ear - ly, ve - ry ear - ly Christ was born.

J. M. Neale

Neale's original version (Cowley Carol Book 4) includes further words to include the tune, *Magnum no-men Domini*, which is printed separately in *Piae Cantiones.*

129. IN DULCI JUBILO

German Mediaeval Carol
harmony from R. L. de Pearsall

1. *In dul - ci ju - bi - lo* ____ Let us our hom - age
1 shew; ____ Our heart's joy re - cli - neth *In prae - se - pi -*
1 - o, ____ And like a bright star shi - neth *Ma - tris in gre - mi -*
1 - o. ____ *Al - pha es et O;* ____ *Al - pha es et O.* ____

2. *O Je - su par - vu - le!* ____ My heart is sore for
2. thee! ____ Hear me I be - seech thee, *O pu - er op - ti -*
2. - me! ____ My pray - er let it reach thee, *O Prin - ceps glo - ri -*
2. - ae! ____ *Tra - he me post te;* ____ *Tra - he me post te!* ____

3. *O Pa - tris ca - ri - tas!* ____ *O Na - ti le - ni -*
3. - tas! ____ Deep - ly were we stain - èd *Per no - stra cri - mi -*
3. - na; ____ But thou hast for us gain - èd *Coe - lo - rum gau - di -*
3. - a. ____ O that we were there; ____ O that we were there! ____

4. *U - bi sunt gau - di - a* ____ If that they be not
4. there? ____ An - gels there are sing - ing *No - va can - ti -*
4. - ca, ____ Sweet bells the while a - ring - ing *In re - gis cu - ri -*
4. - a: ____ O that we were there; ____ O that we were there! ____

178

130. GOOD CHRISTIAN MEN, REJOICE

In Dulci Jubilo

Moderately quick

Old German Melody (J.S.)

1 Good Chris-tian men, re - joice___ With heart and soul_ and voice!___ Give ye heed to what we say: Je - sus Christ is born to-day. Ox and ass be - fore Him bow, And He is in the man-ger now: Christ is born to - day, ___ Christ is born to - day.___

2 Good Christian men, rejoice
With heart and soul and voice!
Now ye hear of endless bliss:
Jesus Christ was born for this.
He hath oped the heavenly door,
And man is blessed for evermore.
Christ was born for this.

3 Good Christian men, rejoice
With heart and soul and voice!
Now ye need not fear the grave:
Jesus Christ was born to save;
Calls you one, and calls you all,
To gain His everlasting hall.
Christ was born to save.

J. M. Neale

These words were written by J.M. Neale, in imitation of the old carol *In dulci jubilo,* to carry the tune. Originally a two-syllable exclamation followed line 3, but since this was inserted because of a mis-reading of the original tune, it is here omitted. (See E.C. pp 195)

179

131. O'ER THE HILL AND O'ER THE VALE

In Vernali Tempore

Piae Cantiones, 1582
(G.R.W.)

1 O'er— the hill—and o'er—the vale, Come three kings to-ge-ther,
  Car-ing nought for snow—and hail, Cold and wind and wea-ther;
  Now on Per-sia's sand-y plains, Now where Ti-gris swells with rains,
  They—their cam-els te-ther: Now thro' Sy-rian lands they go,
  Now—thro' Mo-ab, faint—and slow, Now—o'er E-dom's hea-ther.

2 O'er the hill and o'er the vale,
  Each king bears a present:
  Wise men go a Child to hail,
  Monarchs seek a Peasant:
  And a star in front proceeds,
  Over rocks and rivers leads,
  Shines with beams incessant:
  Therefore onward, onward still!
  Ford the stream and climb the hill:
  Love makes all things pleasant.

3 He is God ye go to meet:
  Therefore incense proffer:
  He is King ye go to greet;
  Gold is in your coffer:
  Also Man, He comes to share
  Ev'ry woe that man can bear —
  Tempter, Railer, Scoffer:
  Therefore now, against the day,
  In the grave when Him they lay
  Myrrh ye also offer.

J. M. Neale

180

132. SLEEP, MY LITTLE ONE
Schlaf, mein Kindelein

German
(G.H.)

Softly - lulling

1. "Sleep, my lit - tle one, Sleep, my dear - est one,"
"Sleep, sweet babe di - vine, Rest, O treas - ure mine,

2. "Slum - ber through the night, Till the morn - ing light,
Thee dear child I will, keep from harm and ill,

3. Born in cat - tle stall, Yet the Hope of all,
Je - sus man's best friend, Let Thy peace de-scend,

Ma - ry thus sings un - to her boy.
Slum - ber my com - fort and my joy."

Co - si - ly fold - ing Thy hands in mine."
Babe in the man - ger a - mid the kine."
Now to the world sweet com - fort bring;
Fall - ing from heav'n on si - lent wing.

REFRAIN

High in the heav'ns the an - gels now are sing - ing,

Lul - la, lul - la, lul - la - by.

Gordon Hitchcock

181

133. THE HOUSE OF BREAD

In Einem Kripplein

Melody from
H. von Laufenberg's MS. c. 1430
(E.R.)

1 A - wake from sleep, the night is spent! The morning star moves up the sky;
2 While man, the ra-ther sin to choose, Prepares the pur-ple, plants the thorn,

The hosts of heav'n, with sweet con-sent, Pro-claim sal-va-tion's time is high:
The Word of God our flesh en-dues That we, by will of God re-born,

Come, praise the long — im-plored, Our Sa-viour Christ — the Lord!
The sons of God — may be, To all e - ter - ni - ty.

3 Let regal power and humble beast
   And shepherd, serving both, attend;
   Since all, from greatest unto least,
   Are proffered bliss which shall not end,
   Where spreads His banquet-board
   Our Saviour, Christ the Lord.

4 In Bethlehem, the House of Bread,
   A richer harvest now is sown;
   For none at Jesus' Table fed
   Shall ever thirst or hunger own,
   But shall from foes be free
   To all eternity.

5 Greet the fulfilment of your dreams,
   Sad earth, by Adam's plague oppressed!
   May He whose lowliness redeems
   Both north and south, both east and west,
   Now be by all adored,
   Our Saviour, Christ the Lord.

T. C. Micklem

(v. 4) 'Beth-lehem' means in Hebrew 'House of bread'

134. QUEM PASTORES

Shepherds tell your beauteous story

Latin words and melody from a
Hohenfurt M.S. of the 15th cent.

1 Shep - herds tell your beau - teous sto - ry
2 Beth - le - hem hath now be - hold - en

3 So with Ma - ry's glad - ness blend - ing,
4 God with us, thro' Ma - ry dwell - eth!

How the dazz - ling an - gel glo - ry Sang to Ju - da's
Kings of tribes far off and old - en, In - cense, myrrh and

Let our thank - ful - ness as - cend - ing Scale high heav'n in
This dear grace all praise ex - cell - eth, Let the song such

hill - sides hoa - ry, "Born is your E - ter - nal King"
mea - sure gold - en To her conqu'ring Li - on bring.

sweet con - tending, With the an - gels' glor - ious choir.
bliss that tell - eth In its own great joy ex - pire.

J. O'Connor

183

135. I KNOW A FLOWER
Es ist ein' Ros' entsprungen

Melody 15th century
Harmonised by Michael Prætorius
1609

M. ♩ = about 60

1. I know a flow'r it spring-eth From earth a ten-der
shoot: As old-en pro-phet sing-eth, From Jes-se came the
root That bore a blos-som bright, In depth of chil-ly
win-ter A-bout the dead of night.

2. This plant, with blossom la-den, As spake E-say of
yore, Is Ma-ry, spot-less maid-en, For us this flow'-ret
bore; By God's e-ter-nal will, A seem-ly Babe she
child-eth, Yet maid re-main-eth still.

3. Praise, hon-our, to the Fa-ther, The Son, the Spi-rit
blest; And Ma-ry, God's own Mo-ther, For help we make re-
quest: Be-seech thy dear-est Son That He would be our
Re-fuge And shrive us, ev-ery one.

G. R. Woodward

136. THIS DAY IS BORN EMMANUEL

En natus est Emanuel

M. Praetorius 1609

1 This day is born Em - ma - nu - el, God with us! ___
As ___ fore - told by Ga - bri - el; God with us!
God with us! ___ A Sa - viour Christ the Lord.

1 En na - tus est E - man - u - el, Do - mi - nus! ___
Quem ___ prae - di - xit Ga - bri - el, Do - mi - nus!
Do - mi - nus ___ Sal - va - tor no - ster est.

2 Behold Him in the manger lie,
    God with us!
Th'admirable Child most high,
    God with us, God with us,
A Saviour Christ the Lord.

3 Upsprings for us the day of days,
    God with us!
By the Virgin Mary's grace,
    God with us, God with us,
A Saviour Christ the Lord.

4 Praise we the Father, praise the Son,
    God with us!
Holy Spirit, Three in One.
    God with us, God with us,
A Saviour Christ the Lord.

2 Hic jacet in praesepio,
    Dominus!
Puer admirabilis,
    Dominus!
Dominus Salvator noster est.

3 Haec lux est orta hodie,
    Dominus!
Ex Maria virgine,
    Dominus!
Dominus Salvator noster est.

4 Laudetur Pater, Filius,
    Dominus!
Et Sacratus Spiritus,
    Dominus!
Dominus Salvator noster est.

Tr. J. O'Connor

137. ST. LUKE'S CAROL

German folksong
arr. J. BRAHMS

1. The shep - herds in the fields at night Were
2. The an - gel set their fears at naught, Good
3. No room was at the inn that day But
4. And sud - den - ly, a mul - ti - tude Of
5. The shep - herds found, with - out de - lay, The
6. Then prais - ing God, they spread a - broad The

star - tled by a glor - ious sight, For lo, up - on their

2. tid - ings of great joy he brought:- A Sav - iour now in
3. safe with - in a man - ger lay, In swadd - ling clothes, the
4. heav - en's host be - side him stood. Their prais - es rang through
5. man - ger where the Christ Child lay. All wrapp'd in swadd - ling
6. joy - ful news of Christ the Lord. Let us re - call that

watch and ward, Came the an - gel of__ the Lord!

2. Beth - le - hem, Je - sus Christ, was born to them!
3. Babe di - vine- This the an - gel gave for sign.
4. field and fen:- "Peace on earth, good will to - ward men!"
5. clothes was He- This the sign for them to see.
6. joy a - gain:- "Peace on earth, good will to - ward men!"

In ex - cel - sis De - o, glor - i - a!____

In ex - cel - sis De - o, glor - i - a!____

Laurence H. Davies

186

138. SUSANI

German carol melody from
KATHARINA TIRS' *Hymnarius*
(R.T.)

1 From high-est heaven come, an-gels come! _ E - ya! _
2 And tune your mer-ry lay, ('tis meet) _ E - ya! _

3 Blend with your voi-ces, where ye sing _ E - ya! _
4 Sing peace on earth, from shore to shore, _ E - ya! _

E - ya! Su-sa-ni, su-sa-ni, su - sa-ni; With
E - ya! Su-sa-ni, su-sa-ni, su - sa-ni; To

E - ya! Su-sa-ni, su-sa-ni, su - sa-ni; The
E - ya! Su-sa-ni, su-sa-ni, su - sa-ni; And

jo - cund song; with fife _ and drum. } Al - le - lu - ia, Al -
harp _ and lute _ and vi - ol sweet. }

or - gan and _ the trem - bling string. } Al - le - lu - ia, Al -
praise _ your Lord _ for ev - er - more. }

-le - lu - ia. _ Of Je - sus sing _ and Ma - ri - a.

tr. D.N.Y.

Words from *Niederdeutsche Geistliche Lieder* (1524) cf. 92
'Susani' = 'Hosanna'.
See words edition for original German text.

187

139. SHEPHERDS ARE SINGING

Hirtenlied

Tyrolean Melody
(E.R.)

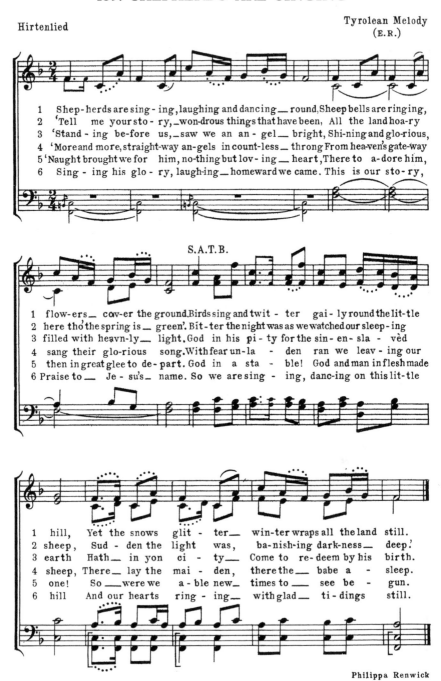

1 Shep-herds are sing-ing, laughing and dancing round, Sheep bells are ringing,
2 'Tell me your sto-ry, won-drous things that have been, All the land hoa-ry
3 'Stand-ing be-fore us, saw we an an-gel bright, Shi-ning and glo-rious,
4 'More and more, straight-way an-gels in count-less throng From hea-ven's gate-way
5 'Naught brought we for him, no-thing but lov-ing heart, There to a-dore him,
6 Sing-ing his glo-ry, laugh-ing homeward we came. This is our sto-ry,

S.A.T.B.

1 flow-ers cov-er the ground, Birds sing and twit-ter gai-ly round the lit-tle
2 here tho' the spring is green'. Bit-ter the night was as we watched our sleep-ing
3 filled with heavn-ly light. God in his pi-ty for the sin-en-sla-vèd
4 sang their glo-rious song. With fear un-la-den ran we leav-ing our
5 then in great glee to de-part. God in a sta-ble! God and man in flesh made
6 Praise to Je-su's name. So we are sing-ing, danc-ing on this lit-tle

1 hill, Yet the snows glit-ter win-ter wraps all the land still.
2 sheep, Sud-den the light was, ba-nish-ing dark-ness deep.'
3 earth Hath in yon ci-ty Come to re-deem by his birth.
4 sheep, There lay the mai-den, there the babe a-sleep.
5 one! So were we a-ble new times to see be-gun.
6 hill And our hearts ring-ing with glad ti-dings still.

Philippa Renwick

140. THE SHADOWS ARE FALLING

Tyrolean Cradle Song

1   The shadows are falling, the evening's at hand,
    To watch by the cradle, my Saviour, I stand:
    A song I am singing, to lull Thee to sleep,
    Oh, rest now from crying: safe guard I will keep.
    Oh, sleep; oh, rest, Thou sweetest and best!

2   Forget for a moment the sorrows of earth,
    Man's burden of sin that Thou bearest from birth;
    Forget the poor stable where Thou must rest,
    If Thou dost accept it, no palace so blest.
    Oh, sleep; oh, rest, Thou sweetest and best.

3   Thy glory gives grace to the manger and stall,
    On me at Thy side may a benison fall:
    Thus blest with Thy presence, 'tis here I would be,
    Child Jesus, my Saviour, n'er parted from Thee.
    Oh, sleep; oh, rest, Thou sweetest and best.

Paraphrase by T. Armstrong

189

141. SHEPHERDS' CRADLE SONG

Schlaf wohl, du Himmelsknabe du

KARL LEUNER. 1814
(G. G.)

Andante moderato e teneramente

1. O slum-ber heaven-ly trea-sure, now, Sleep well, thou dar-ling child; While

2. Lo, Ma - ry now with lov-ing hand Hath laid thee down to sleep, While
3. When thou shalt grow to man's es-tate Gol-goth-a wait-eth thee, Where

an - gel wings shall fan thy brow With gen-tle mo-tion mild.___ We

Jo - seph at thy head doth stand A faith-ful watch to keep. Now
men shall seize thee in their hate And nail thee to a tree. But

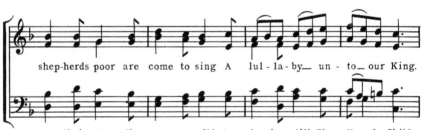

shep-herds poor are come to sing A lul - la - by___ un - to___ our King.

on their straw the ox - en mild Are ly - ing still, Sleep Ho - ly Child.
now sweet dreams be thine to-night, Sleep Ho - ly Babe till morn-ing light.

Lul - la - by,___ Lul - la - by,___ Sleep, sleep soft-ly lul - la - by.

(Lul - la, lul-la-by, Lul - la, lul-la-by)

John Davies

190

142. SILENT NIGHT, HOLY NIGHT
Stille Nacht, Heilige Nacht

FRANZ GRÜBER
(G.G.)

1 *Stille Nacht, heilige Nacht,*
Alles schläft, einsam wacht,
Nur das traute, hochheilige Paar
Holder Knabe in lockigen Haar
Schlafe in himlicher Ruh,
Schlafe in himlicher Ruh.

2 *Stille Nacht, heilige Nacht,*
Hirten erst Kundgemacht,
Durch der Engel Halleluja
Tänt es laut von fern und nah,
Christ der Retter ist da
Christ der Retter ist da.

3 *Stille Nacht heilige Nacht,*
Gottes Sohn o wie lacht
Lieb aus deinem Göttlichen Mund,
Da uns schlägt die rettende Stund.
Christ in deiner Geburt,
Christ in deiner Geburt.

Joseph Mohr, 1792–1848

1 Silent night, Holy night,
All is calm, all is bright;
'Round yon virgin mother and Child,
Holy Infant so tender and mild,
Sleep in heavenly peace,
Sleep in heavenly peace.

2 Silent night, Holy night,
Shepherds quake at the sight;
Glories stream from heaven afar,
Heav'nly hosts sing Alleluia!
Christ the Saviour is born!
Christ the Saviour is born!

3 Silent night, Holy night,
Son of God, love's pure light;
Radiance beams from Thy holy face,
With the dawn of redeeming grace,
Jesus, Lord, at thy birth,
Jesus, Lord, at thy birth.

Tr. Anon.

143. OUR LADY ON CHRISTMAS EVE

Dutch Carol of the 15th cent.
(R.T.)

1 Our Lady on Christmas Eve had to go To
2 It hailed and it snowed, it grew very cold, The

3 Said Mary, I'm weary and fain would I stay, But
4 A little way on, to a stable they came No

Bethlehem___ in frost___ and snow; Saint
rime___ was hoar___ on field___ and fold; Saint

let us go further along___ the way, There's
door___ no hearth_ the cold, ___ to tame, And

Joseph went too, To show her the way And
Joseph said: Ah what e'er shall I do? If

something that tells me a hut is near by And
so the Lord Jesus was born___ that night Where

bring her secure___ to Christ___ mas Day.
so we go on ___ what happens to you?

that is less bleak___ than o - pen sky
David was promised glory and might.

tr. J. O'Connor

192

144. IN A CAVERN, OXEN TROD

Een Soudaen had een Dochterken

Dutch melody
(J.R.L.)

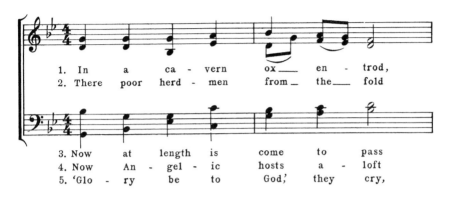

1. In a ca - vern ox___ en - trod,
2. There poor herd - men from___ the___ fold

3. Now at length is come to pass
4. Now An - gel - ic hosts a - loft
5. 'Glo - ry be to God,' they cry,

Je - su Christ, Thou li - est,___ In a man - ger,
Bend the knee be - fore Thee:___ There with in - cense,

That which had been told - en, Touch - ing_Christ and_
Cleave the sky a - sun - der, Ca - rol - ling, in_
'God, who con - de - scend-est To be_ born; who_

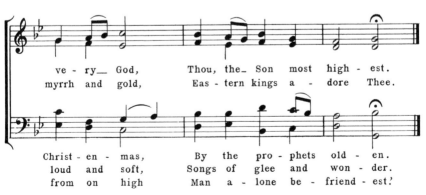

ve - ry_ God, Thou, the_ Son most high - est.
myrrh and gold, Eas - tern kings a - dore Thee.

Christ - en - mas, By the pro - phets old - en.
loud and soft, Songs of glee and won - der.
from on high Man a - lone be - friend - est.'

tr. G. R. Woodward

193

145. WITHIN A STABLE

Dutch
(G. H.)

1 With - in a sta - ble lay a maid - en, Vir - gin
A joy and com - fort to sweet Ma - ry God hath
2 St. Jo - seph watch'd the Babe in won - der, All be -
For now to dwell - ing place so hum - ble Had there

3 All through the night St. Jo - seph wan - der'd Seek - ing
And with their breath the pa - tient ox - en warm'd the

pure and fair was she;
sent his Son to be. Yet this Ba - by, laid in
wild - ered as he stood; Still a - mid the ox - en's
come God's great - est good.

fu - el for the shed; And in Ma - ry's ten - der
air round Je - su's bed;

man - ger, Wept as if__ He knew the dan - ger. Sleep, O
low - ing Were the In - fant's tears soft flow - ing. Sleep, O

keep - ing, Je - sus ceased His si - lent weep - ing, Sleep, O

sleep, my lit - tle one sleep, An - gels si - lent watch o'er you keep.
sleep, my lit - tle one sleep, An - gels si - lent watch o'er you keep.

sleep, my lit - tle one sleep, An - gels si - lent watch o'er you keep.

Irene Gass

146. HAIL, BLESSED VIRGIN MARY

Italian Carol (1689)
(c.w.)

1 Hail, bles-sed vir-gin Ma - ry, For so when he did meet thee Spake migh-ty Gab-ri - el, and thus we greet thee; Come weal, come woe, our hymn shall ne - ver va - ry, Hail bles - sed Vir - gin Ma - ry, Hail bles-sed Vir-gin Ma - ry!

2 A - ve, a - ve Ma - ri - a! To glad-den priest and peo - ple The an - ge-lus shall ring from ev - 'ry stee - ple, To sound His vir-gin birth, Al - le - lu - i - a, A - ve, a - ve Ma - ri - a, A - ve, a - ve Ma - ri - a!

3 Arch - an-gels chant O - san - na and Ho - ly, Ho - ly, Ho - ly Be - fore the In - fant born of thee, thou low - ly, Aye— mai - den child of Jo - a - chim and An - na, Arch - an - gels chant O - san - na, Arch - an - gels chant O - san - na!

G. R. Woodward

147. DARK IS THE EVEN

Su levate pastori

Italian melody (La Rosellina)
from "Laude Spirituali," 1674
(R.T.)

1 Dark is the e - ven', Yet is the hea - ven Light-ed and
2 Fair ro - ses grow - ing Mid win - ter's snow - ing, Who hath the
3 O - ver His dream - ing Ra-diance is stream - ing, Flood-ing the

4 From God de - scen - ded, Rag - ged, un - ten - ded, Birds in the
5 Cat - tle are call - ing There in His stall - ing: Jo - seph and
6 Me - lo - dies ring - ing, An - gels are sing - ing, Songs all a -

glow ing a - round __ us. Shep-herds a - ris - ing
vi - sion be - hold - en? Yet, o'er the mea - dows
de - so - late man - ger! In Ma - ry's keep - ing

branch - es a - bove __ them Warm-er are bid - ing,
Ma - ry are keep - ing Watch o'er His mov - ing,
- round us are swell - ing: "Sun of the morn - ing!

In wild sur-mis - ing, "Ma-gic in - deed __ hath found us."
Through mid-night's sha - dows See! how the sun __ is gold - en! __
Soft He is sleep-ing, Held in her arms __ from dan - ger. __

Safe in their hid - ing, Clothed by the hands __ that love them!
Faith-ful and lov - ing; Hap - py the Babe __ is sleep - ing.
Ten-der Thy dawn-ing! Dark-ness and ill __ dis - pel - ling

Tr. K. W. Simpson

148. TO WEARY SHEPHERDS SLEEPING

Italian carol from *"Laude Spirituali"* 1674
(R. T.)

1 To wea - ry shep-herds sleep - ing, A blind - ing light ap -
2 With sil - ver wings and gold - en A might - y host they

3 And while His words they pon - der, The an - gel host a -
4 In joy they turned their fac - es To where they heard He
5 Their gifts they laid a - round Him With shy and hum - ble

- peared; And from their couch - es leap - ing, They
saw: Ne'er had their eyes be - hold - en Such

- round Cried: "In a man - ger yon - der The
lay, And mer - ry were their pa - ces And
word, And hap - py to have found Him They

scat - ter'd, all a - fear'd; But Ga - briel spake to
ma - jes - ty be - fore. Said Ga - bri - el that

King of Kings is found! Go shep - herds, do not
songs up - on the way. And when the dawn was
lin - gered and a - dored. (While Ga - briel up - ward

calm them From all that did a - larm them.
ev - en: "I come from God in Hea - ven."

tar - ry; Your lov - ing hom - age car - ry."
creep - ing They found Him sweet - ly sleep - ing.
wing - ing "Now Peace on Earth!" was sing - ing.)

tr. by K.W. Simpson.

197

149. CAROL OF THE BAGPIPERS
Il Zampognari

Neapolitan melody
(E.R.)

1 When Je - sus Christ our Lord ⸻ Was born at Beth - le -

- hem, ⸻ The stars that night were gleam - ing

O - ver combe and down. Si - lent-ly giv - ing Signs of the

liv - ing, To ⸻ the folk of Beth - lem town; ⸻ A

bright - er star___ it shone, ___ For Ma - gi far, A

guid - ing___ star that led them on. ___

2   Sweet peace reign'd on the earth the night of Jesus's birth,
The lion with lamb was lying,
Bear with calf did roam.
Close-by the shepherd
Wandered the leopard,
Every beast with Man at home,
Things great and small were one;
For lamb that night
No screaming fright, but Joy did come.

3   While shepherds watch did keep, o'er all their drowsing sheep,
From heav'n a voice came singing :
"Peace, Goodwill befall".
Come and adore Him,
Kneel down before Him;
Seek the Babe in yonder stall,
Your King though weak and small,
For He this night
A lasting Light now shines for all.

Pr. Gordon Hitchcock

150. SLEEP, MY SAVIOUR, SLEEP

Bohemian folk-melody
(G.G. and E.P.)

Slowly and smoothly

1. Sleep, my Sa - viour, sleep, On Thy bed of hay, —
2. Sleep, my Sa - viour, sleep, On Thy bed of hay, —

An - gels in the span - gled Hea - ven Sing their glad-some
'Ere the mourn-ing An - gel com - eth To the moon-lit

Christ - mas car - ols Till the dawn of day.
o - live gar - den, Wip - ing tears a - way.

3. Sleep, my Saviour sleep
   Sweet on Mary's breast,
   Now the Shepherds kneel adoring,
   Now the Mother's heart is joyous,
   Take a happy rest.

4. Sleep, my Saviour sleep
   Sweet on Mary's breast,
   Crucified, with wounds and bruises,
   Bleeding, purple, stained, disfigured,
   One day Thou wilt rest.

S. Baring-Gould

200

151. TO MAKE HIM SLEEP

Czech Carol
(G. G.)

Softly, lilting

1 To make him sleep his Moth - er sang___ Sweet lul - la - by,
2 I have pre - par'd your hum - ble bed,___ My Lord and King,

Gent - ly she rock'd her lit - tle child,___ Sleep, hush-a - bye.
Sum-moned all crea-tures round your head___ And birds on wing.

My dear - est ba - by, God's own son, Go to sweet byes;
Oh, sleep and rest, my darl - ing boy, My tur - tle dove,

Sleep soft-ly, sleep, my love - ly one, Close your dear eyes.
Go to sweet byes, my pride, my joy, My dear-est love.

C. K. Offer

201

152. INFANT HOLY
W zlobie Lezy

Polish Carol tune
(G. H.)

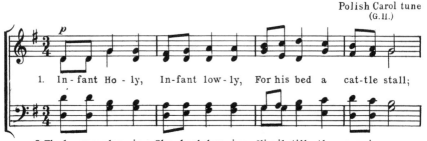

1. In-fant Ho-ly, In-fant low-ly, For his bed a cat-tle stall;

2. Flocks were sleep-ing, Shep-herds keep-ing Vig-il till the morn-ing new

Ox-en low-ing, Lit-tle know-ing Christ the Babe is Lord of all.

Saw the glo-ry, Heard the sto-ry, Tid-ings of a gos-pel true.

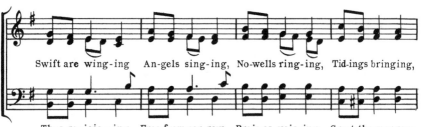

Swift are wing-ing An-gels sing-ing, No-wells ring-ing, Tid-ings bringing,

Thus re-joic-ing, Free from sor-row, Prais-es voic-ing, Greet the mor-row,

last time **pp**

Christ the Babe is Lord of all. *(Hummed)* *morendo*

Christ the Babe was born for you!

tr E. M. G. Reed

*Optional ending

202

153. STEEPLES, SET YOUR BELLS A-RINGING

Russian Carol
Adapted from "Dalekaya i blezkaya"
ALFRED WHITEHEAD

Fast and very cheerful

1 Stee-ples, set your bells a-ring-ing, Clang-ing bells a - ring - ing;
2 Ev-'ry bell its loud-est peal-ing, Clang-ing, swing ing, peal - ing,
3 Ev-'ry man his voice up-rais-ing, Glad, his voice up - rais - ing;

Church-es, set your choirs a - sing - ing, Joy - ful choirs a - sing - ing.
Ev - 'ry stee-ple now a - reel-ing, Joy - ful - ly a - reel - ing.
Ev - 'ry man his Sa - viour prais-ing, Joy - ful, Christ a - prais - ing.

Christ is come to save man-kind, Christ is born to save us!

(V.3.ff rall.)

Stee-ples, church-es, ring-ing, sing-ing, Christ is come to save us!

Alfred Whitehead

* A natural last time

203

154. CHRISTMAS EVE

Melody by PETER KNUDSEN
(E.R.)

1 Oh, glad I am 'tis Christ - mas eve, The
2 So let us deck the Christ - mas tree With
3 And his bright Star is shin - ing still And
4 So that is why each Christ - mas eve, In

night of Je - su's birth; __ A Star shone bright that
can - dles shin - ing clear. __ And each a star that
nev - er will grow dim __ It lights us all up -
ca - rols and in mirth, __ We cel - e - brate the

ho - ly night And Christ came here (up)-on earth. __
shone a - far, Up - on our Sa - viour dear. __
- on our way And leads us up __ to Him. __
Ho - ly Child; His com - ing here (up)-on earth. __

G. Grimes

155. ONCE IN ROYAL DAVID'S CITY

IRBY

H. J. GAUNTLETT
Harmonised by A. H. Mann

1 Once in royal David's city
   Stood a lowly cattle shed,
Where a mother laid her baby
   In a manger for his bed:
Mary was that Mother mild,
Jesus Christ her little Child.

2 He came down to earth from heaven
   Who is God and Lord of all,
And his shelter was a stable,
   And his cradle was a stall;
With the poor and mean and lowly
Lived on earth our Saviour holy.

3 And through all his wondrous childhood
   He would honour and obey,
Love and watch the lowly Maiden,
   In whose gentle arms he lay:
Christian children all must be,
Mild, obedient, good as he.

4 For he is our childhood's pattern,
   Day by day like us he grew,
He was little, weak, and helpless,
   Tears and smiles like us he knew:
And he feeleth for our sadness,
And he shareth in our gladness.

5 And our eyes at last shall see him,
   Through his own redeeming love,
For that Child so dear and gentle
   Is our Lord in heaven above;
And he leads his children on
To the place where he is gone.

6 Not in that poor lowly stable,
   With the oxen standing by,
We shall see him; but in heaven,
   Set at God's right hand on high;
Where like stars his children crowned
All in white shall wait around.

Cecil Frances Alexander

205

156. HARK! THE HERALD ANGELS SING

Felix Mendelssohn-Bartholdy
(D.E.)

In moderate time

1 Hark! the her-ald an-gels sing, 'Glo-ry to the new-born King,

Peace on earth, and mer-cy mild, God and sin-ners re-con-ciled!'

Joy-ful, all ye na-tions, rise, Join the tri-umph of the skies,

With th' an-gel-ic host pro-claim, 'Christ is born in Beth-le-hem.'

REFRAIN   Unison

Hark! the her-ald an-gels sing, 'Glo-ry to the new-born King.'

Org.

2 Christ, by highest heaven adored,
Christ, the everlasting Lord,
Late in time behold Him come,
Offspring of a virgin's womb.
Veiled in flesh the Godhead see;
Hail, the Incarnate Deity,
Pleased as Man with man to dwell,
Jesus, our Immanuel!

> *Hark! the herald angels sing,*
> *'Glory to the new-born King.'*

3 Hail, the heaven-born Prince of Peace!
Hail, the Sun of Righteousness!
Light and life to all He brings,
Risen with healing in His wings.
Mild He lays His glory by,
Born that man no more may die,
Born to raise the sons of earth,
Born to give them second birth.

> *Hark! the herald angels sing,*
> *'Glory to the new-born King.'*

Charles Wesley, 1707-88

The tune was originally adapted by W.H. Cummings from a chorus in Mendelssohn's Festgesang (1844).
The version above preserves the popular (though not the original) form of the melody, but
does not, like most, insist on the unison singing of the tune throughout.

H

157. IT CAME UPON A MIDNIGHT CLEAR

Noel

from an English traditional melody
Arr. by Arthur Seymour Sullivan

1 It came upon the midnight clear,
   That glorious song of old,
From angels bending near the earth
   To touch their harps of gold:
'Peace on the earth, goodwill to men,
   From heaven's all-gracious King!'
The world in solemn stillness lay
   To hear the angels sing.

2 Still through the cloven skies they come,
   With peaceful wings unfurled;
And still their heavenly music floats
   O'er all the weary world;
Above its sad and lowly plains
   They bend on hovering wing;
And ever o'er its Babel sounds
   The blessèd angels sing.

3 Yet with the woes of sin and strife
   The world has suffered long;
Beneath the angel-strain have rolled
   Two thousand years of wrong;
And man, at war with man, hear not
   The love-song which they bring:
O hush the noise, ye men of strife,
   And hear the angels sing.

4 For lo, the days have hastened on,
   By prophets seen of old,
And with the ever-circling years
   Came round the day foretold,
When men, surprised by joy, adored
   The prince of peace, their King;
Come, all who hear! Join in the song
   Which men and angels sing.

E. H. Sears.
verse 4 altered

The original contained 5 verses, of which one is here omitted. The last verse (which may be found in most hymn books) we have altered, being of the opinion that in its original form it was sufficiently misleading theologically to mar an otherwise excellent hymn. The tune is an extension and arrangement of Eardisley, (see *O.B.C.Ap.5*) which was first noted in Herefordshire.

158. O COME, ALL YE FAITHFUL

MS. of J. F. WADE (1711-86)

Moderato

mf 1. O come, all ye faith-ful, Joy-ful and tri-um-phant, O

2. God of — God, — Light — of — Light, —
3. Sing, choirs of An - gels, Sing in ex - ul - ta - tion,
(Unison) 4. Yea, Lord, we greet Thee, Born this hap - py morn - ing,

1. come — ye, O come — ye to Beth - - le - hem;

2. Lo! He ab - hors — not the Vir - gin's womb;
3. Sing, all ye ci - ti - zens of hea - ven a - bove;
4. Je - su, to Thee — be — glo - ry given;

1. Come and — be - hold — Him, Born the King of An - gels;

2. Ve - ry — God, Be - got - ten, not cre - a - ted:
3. Glo - ry to God — In — the — high - est:
4. Word of the Fa - ther, Now in flesh ap - pear - ing:

REFRAIN

p O come let us a - dore Him, O come let us a - dore Him, O

come let us a - dore — Him, — Christ — the Lord.

See words edition for original Latin text.

18th century Latin hymn
tr. F. Oakeley

159. AS WITH GLADNESS MEN OF OLD

Adapted from a chorale by
KONRAD KOCHER (1786-1872)

1 As with gladness men of old
Did the guiding star behold,
As with joy they hailed its light,
Leading onward, beaming bright,—
So, most gracious Lord, may we
Evermore be led to Thee.

2 As with joyful steps they sped,
To that lowly manger-bed,
There to bend the knee before
Thee, whom heaven and earth adore,—
So may we with willing feet
Ever seek Thy mercy-seat.

3 As they offered gifts most rare
At that manger rude and bare,—
So may we with holy joy,
Pure, and free from sin's alloy,
All our costliest treasures bring,
Christ, to Thee, our heavenly King.

4 Holy Jesus, every day
Keep us in the narrow way;
And, when earthly things are past,
Bring our ransomed souls at last
Where they need no star to guide,
Where no clouds Thy glory hide.

5 In the heavenly country bright
Need they no created light;
Thou its light, its joy, its crown,
Thou its sun which goes not down;
There for ever may we sing
Hallelujahs to our King.

William Chatterton Dix

160. BRIGHTEST AND BEST

Liebster Immanuel

Later form of melody from *Himmels-Lust*, 1679
J. S. BACH

1 Brightest and best of the sons of the morning,
   Dawn on our darkness and lend us Thine aid;
Star of the east, the horizon adorning,
   Guide where our Infant Redeemer is laid.

2 Cold on His cradle the dew-drops are shining,
   Low lies His head with the beasts of the stall:
Angels adore Him in slumber reclining,
   Maker and Monarch and Saviour of all.

3 Say, shall we yield Him, in costly devotion,
   Odours of Edom and offerings divine?
Gems of the mountain and pearls of the ocean,
   Myrrh from the forest or gold from the mine.

4 Vainly we offer each ample oblation,
   Vainly with gifts would, each favour secure;
Richer by far is the heart's adoration
   Dearer to God are the prayers of the poor.

5 Brightest and best of the sons of the morning,
   Dawn on our darkness and lend us thine aid;
Star of the east, the horizon adorning,
   Guide where our Infant Redeemer is laid.

R. Heber

211

161. ALL MY HEART THIS NIGHT REJOICES

J. G. EBELING 1637-76

1. All my heart this night re - joic - es, As I hear
far and near, Sweet-est an - gel voi - ces: "Christ is
born!" their choirs are sing - ing, Till the air
ev - 'ry - where Now with joy is ring - ing.

2. Hark! a voice from yon - der man - ger, Soft and sweet,
3. Come, then let us hast - en yon - der; Here let all,
4. Thee, O Lord, with heed I'll che - rish, Live to Thee

doth en - treat: "Flee from woe and dan - ger; Breth - ren,
great and small, Kneel in awe and won - der; Love him
and with Thee Dy - ing, shall not pe - rish, But shall

come from all doth grieve you, You are freed;
who with love is yearn - ing; Hail the star
dwell with Thee for ev - er Far on high,

all you need I will sure - ly give you."
that from far Bright with hope is burn - ing.
in the joy That can ne - ver al - ter.

P. Gerhardt 1607-76, tr. Catherine Winkworth

Words from Paul Gerhardt's *Fröhlich soll mein Herze springen* (1653)

212

162. ALL THE SKIES TONIGHT SING O'ER US

Melody by
JOHANN GEORG EBELING. 1666
(J. S. B.)

1 All the skies to - night sing o'er us! Sweet and far Star to star Mak - eth sol - emn chor - us. Time the mid-night blest is tell - ing When our Lord God the World Made with us His dwell - ing.

2 Glory in the highest heaven!
And again
Unto men
Their soul's peace be given!
All our wrong by Him is righted
In Whose birth
Heav'n and earth
Stand for aye united.

3 Sons of men, let nothing grieve you!
Evermore
Heaven's door
Widens to receive you!
Brothers of the Babe Eternal
In His name
Come and claim
Grace and bliss supernal.

P. Gerhardt, 1607-76. tr. J. O'Connor

Another translation of this German hymn appears at No 161

163. O JESUS, SWEET CHILD
O Jesulein Süss

from Schemelli's Gesangbuch
(J. S. B.)

1. O Je - sus, sweet Child, Thou gen - tle and mild! Thy

2. 3. O Je - sus, sweet Child, Thou gen - tle and mild! Thy / The

Fath - er's will Thou hast ful - fill'd. Thou left - est

Fath - er's ang - er hast Thou still'd, Our guilt Thou
earth with glad - ness hast Thou fill'd. Thou cam - est

Heav - en for our sake, And our frail flesh on_

bear - est in our place And win - nest us Thy
down from Heav - en's height, To bring us com - fort

Thee didst take. O Je - sus, sweet Child, Thou gen - tle and mild.

Fath - ers grace. / O Je - sus, sweet Child, Thou gen - tle and mild.
in our night. /

Anon.

214

164. ALL YE WHO ARE TO MIRTH INCLINED

ERIK ROUTLEY

1 All ye who are to mirth inclined, Consider well and bear in mind What our good God for us hath done In sending his beloved Son.
2 Moreover let us ev'ry one Call unto mind and think upon His righteous life, and how he died To have poor sinners justified. Alleluia! Alleluia!
3 There shall you see and hear aright The love of Christ the Lord of might, And how he shed his precious blood Only to do us sinners good. Alleluia! Alleluia!

Traditional

This carol, which selects three verses from a poem originally 28 verses long first printed in *The Garland of Goodwill* (about 1699) is suitable as an Invitatory at a Lent carol service.

215

H*

165. TOMORROW SHALL BE MY DANCING DAY

English traditional
(R.T.)

1 To-mor-row shall be— My danc-ing day; I would My true love
   did— so chance To see the le-gend of My play, To
   call My true love to— the dance.

2 Then was— I born of a Vir-gin pure, Of her I took my
   flesh-ly sub-stance; Thus was I knit to man's na-ture, To
   call My true love to— the dance.

CHORUS

Sing Oh! My love, Oh! My love, My love, My love; This have I done for My true love.

3 In a manger laid and wrapp'd I was,
  So very poor, this was My chance,
  Betwixt an ox and a silly poor ass,
  To call My true love to My dance.
        CHORUS

216

4 Then afterwards baptized I was,
   The Holy Ghost on Me did glance,
   My Father's voice heard from above,
   To call My true love to My dance.
          CHORUS

5 Into the desert I was led,
   Where I fasted without substance;
   The devil bade Me make stones My bread,
   To have Me break My true love's dance.
          CHORUS

6 The Jews on Me they make great suit,
   And with Me made great variance,
   Because they lov'd darkness rather than light
   To call My true love to My dance.
          CHORUS

7 For thirty pence Judas Me sold,
   His covetousness for to advance;
   Mark whom I kiss, the same do hold,
   The same is He shall lead the dance.
          CHORUS

8 Before Pilate the Jews Me brought,
   Where Barabbas had deliverance,
   They scourg'd Me and set Me at nought,
   Judged Me to die to lead the dance
          CHORUS

9 Then on the cross hanged I was,
   Where a spear to My heart did glance,
   There issued forth both water and blood,
   To call My true love to My dance.
          CHORUS

10 Then down to hell I took My way
   For My true love's deliverance,
   And rose again on the third day,
   Up to My true love to the dance.
          CHORUS

11 Then up to heaven I did ascend,
   Where now I dwell in sure substance,
   On the right hand of God, that man
   May come unto the general dance.
          CHORUS

The words and tune of this carol are both taken from Sandys, and are reputed to be of Cornish origin.

166. THE HOLLY AND THE IVY

English traditional
(E.R.)

1 The hol-ly and the i-vy when they are both full
2 The hol-ly bears a blos-som as white as a-ny

3 The hol-ly bears a ber-ry as red as a-ny
4 The hol-ly bears a prick-le as sharp as a-ny
5 The hol-ly bears a bark as bit-ter as a-ny

grown, Of all the trees that are in the wood the hol-ly bears the
flower, And Ma-ry bore sweet Je-sus Christ to be our sweet Sa-

blood, And Ma-ry bore sweet Je-sus Christ to do poor sin-ners
thorn, And Ma-ry bore sweet Je-sus Christ on Christmas day in the
gall, And Ma-ry bore sweet Je-sus Christ for to re-deem us

CHORUS

crown.
-viour. O the ris-ing of the sun and the run-ning of the

good.
morn.
all.

deer; O the play-ing of the mer-ry or-gan, sweet sing-ing in the choir.

The words and melody were first noted by Cecil Sharp from Mrs. Clayton of Chipping Campden, Gloucestershire; the words were supplemented by Mrs. Wyatt of East Harptree, Somerset.

167. SANS DAY CAROL

Cornish Carol
(E.R.)

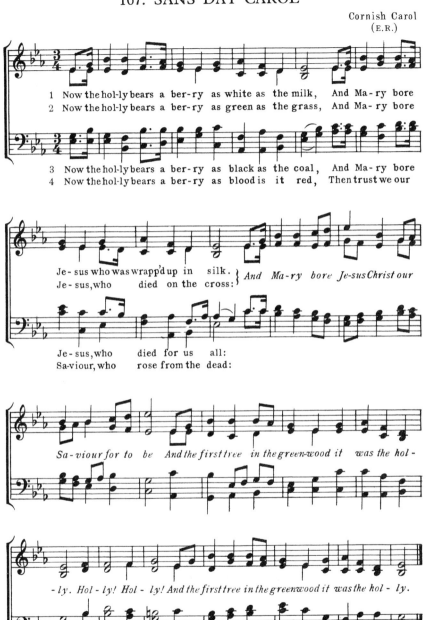

1 Now the hol-ly bears a ber-ry as white as the milk, And Ma-ry bore
2 Now the hol-ly bears a ber-ry as green as the grass, And Ma-ry bore

3 Now the hol-ly bears a ber-ry as black as the coal, And Ma-ry bore
4 Now the hol-ly bears a ber-ry as blood is it red, Then trust we our

Je-sus who was wrapp'd up in silk. } *And Ma-ry bore Je-sus Christ our*
Je-sus, who died on the cross:

Je-sus, who died for us all:
Sa-viour, who rose from the dead:

Sa-viour for to be And the first tree in the green-wood it was the hol-

-ly. Hol-ly! Hol-ly! And the first tree in the greenwood it was the hol-ly.

Words and melody noted by the Rev. G.H.Doble from Mr.W. D.Watson in Cornwall. 'Sans Day' means 'St. Day', a Breton Saint who gave his name to a Cornish village.

219

168. AWAKE, AWAKE YE DROWSY SOULS

Traditional
(E.R.)

With energy

Unison

1 A - wake, a-wake, ye drow-sy souls And hear what I shall tell; Re-

-mem - ber Christ, the Lamb of God Re - deemed our souls from hell. He's

REFRAIN

crown'd with thorns, spit on with scorn, His friends have hid them-selves: *So God*

send you all much joy— in the year, Joy in the year, So God

220

send you all much joy in the year.

r.h.

year.

2 And when his foes had murdered Christ
   And shown their cruel spite,
The sun and moon did hide their heads
   And went in mourning straight:
The heavens stood amazed, and angels gazed
   And the earth was darkened quite:
                   REFRAIN

3 It was early in the morning
   That Mary did him seek;
She saw two angels sitting
   At Jesus' head and feet:
Mary shed tears while Christ appeared
   And he said, 'why dost thou weep?'
                   REFRAIN

4 Then Christ he call-ed Thomas
   And bid him 'Come and see,
And put thy fingers in the wounds
   That are in my body;
And be not faithless, but believe,
   And happy shalt thou be:'
                   REFRAIN

5 Then Christ called his disciples,
   Divided by his death,
And said, 'All powers are given to you
   In heaven and in earth;
Go forth and teach all nations:
   Despise them not,' he saith:
                   REFRAIN

Two dots over a syllable indicate that it must
be sung to two beats: a horizontal bracket
joins two syllables to be sung to one beat.

English traditional carol

221

169. WHEN JESUS CHRIST WAS TWELVE YEARS OLD

Traditional
(R.T.)

1 When Je-sus Christ was twelve years old, As Ho-ly Scrip-ture plain-ly told, _____ He then dis-pu-ted brave and bold A-mongst the learn-ed Doc-tors.

CHORUS

Then praise the Lord, both high and low That He His won-drous works may shew, _____ That we at last to Heav'n may go, Where Christ in glo-ry reign-eth. _____

2 At thirty years He then began
To preach the gospel unto man,
And all Judea wondered then
To hear His heavenly doctrine.
CHORUS

3 Such works He did as made them muse
Amongst the proud hard-hearted Jews,
Yet evermore they did refuse
To own Him for their Saviour.
CHORUS

4 Then first of all, by power divine,
He turnèd water into wine,
When at the Marriage He did dine,
Which made all people wonder.
CHORUS

5 Moreover, with five loaves of bread
Five thousand men He fully fed,
Whereby His glory far was spread
Throughout the land of Jury.
CHORUS

6 The widow's son that dead did lie,
When Christ our Saviour did pass by,
He raised to life immediately,
To her great joy and comfort.
CHORUS

7 Likewise, He heal'd the lepers ten,
Whose bodies were full filthy then,
Yet, not but one return'd again,
His humble thanks to render.
CHORUS

8 The woman that was perplexed sore
With an issue of blood twelve years and more,
Unto her health He did restore,
In the minute of an hour.
CHORUS

9 And more His heavenly might to shew,
Himself upon the sea did go,
There never could a man do so,
But only Christ our Saviour.
CHORUS

10 And yet, for all His wonders great,
The Jews were in a fearful heat
That no persuasion could intreat,
But truly they must kill Him.
CHORUS

11 When they bereav'd His life so good,
The moon was turned into blood,
The earth and temple shaking stood,
And graves full wide did open .
CHORUS

12 Then some of them that stood thereby,
With voices loud began to cry,
This was the Son of God truly,
Without any fear or doubting.
CHORUS

13 For, as He said, it proved so plain,
Within three days He rose again,
Although He suffered bitter pain,
Both death and hell He conquered.
CHORUS

14 Then afterwards ascended He
To heaven in glorious majesty ;
With Him God grant us all to be,
For evermore rejoicing.
CHORUS

Both words and melody are from 'Sandy's'

170. JACOB'S LADDER

English 18th century carol
(E. R.)

1 As Jacob with travel was weary one day, At night on a stone for a pillow he lay; He saw in a vision a ladder so high That its foot was on earth and its top in the sky.

2 This ladder is long, it is strong and well made, Has stood hundreds of years and is not yet decayed; Many millions have climbed it and reach'd Sion's hill And thousands by faith are climbing it still.

3 Come, let us ascend, all may climb it who will;
  For the angels of Jacob are guarding it still;
  And remember, each step that by faith we pass o'er,
  Some prophet or martyr hath trod it before.
                              REFRAIN

4 And when we arrive at the haven of rest
  We shall hear the glad words, 'Come up hither, ye blest;
  Here are regions of light, here are mansions of bliss.'
  O, who would not climb such a ladder as this?
                              REFRAIN

                              Traditional

This carol is a 'Sankey' of the eighteenth century, being made of an old tune set to words which have a clear late-18th century ring about them. But to what words the tune (which is evidently older) was originally set is at present unknown.

171. SUSSEX MUMMERS' CAROL

Sussex tune
(L.E.B.)

Slow

1 O— mor-tal man, re - mem-ber well, When Christ our Lord was
2 O— mor-tal man, re - mem-ber well, When Christ died on the

born,— He was cru-ci-fied be-tween two thieves, And crown-èd with the
rood,— 'Twas for our sins and wick-ed ways Christ shed his pre-cious

thorn,— And crown - èd with— the thorn.
blood,— Christ shed— his pre - cious blood.

3 O mortal man, remember well,
  When Christ was wrapped in clay,
  He was taken to a sepulchre
  Where no man ever lay.

4 God bless the mistress of this house
  With gold chain round her breast;
  Where e'er her body sleeps or wakes,
  Lord, send her soul to rest.

5 God bless the master of this house
  With happiness beside;
  Where e'er his body rides or walks
  Lord Jesus be his guide.

6 God bless your house, your children too,
  Your cattle and your store;
  The Lord increase you day by day,
  And send you more and more.

Traditional

172. REMEMBER, O THOU MAN

THOS. RAVENSCROFT, 1611

1 Re - mem - ber, O thou man, O thou man, O thou man,
2 Re - mem - ber God's good - ness, O thou man, O thou man,

Re - mem - ber, O thou man, Thy time is spent:
Re - mem - ber God's good - ness And prom - ise made:

Re - mem - ber, O thou man, How thou cam'st to me then,
Re - mem - ber God's good - ness, How his on - ly Son he sent,

And I did what I can, There - fore re - pent.
Our sins for to re - dress: Be not a - fraid.

3 The angels all did sing,
   O thou man, O thou man,
The angels all did sing,
   On Sion hill:
The angels all did sing
Praise to our heavenly King,
And peace to man living,
   With right good will.

4 In Bethlem was he born,
   O thou man, O thou man,
In Bethlem was he born,
   For mankind dear:
In Bethlem was he born
For us that were forlorn,
And therefore took no scorn,
   Our sins to bear.

Ravenscroft, *Melismata*, 1611

173. THE MOON SHINES BRIGHT
(Waits Carol)

English traditional

mp 1. The moon shines bright and the stars give a light A

2. A - wake, a - wake good peo - ple all, A -
3. O fair, O fair Je - ru - sa - lem, When
4. The fields were green as green could be When
5. And for the sav - ing of our souls Christ
6. The life of man is but a span And
7. My song is done I must be gone I can

lit-tle be - fore the day, The Lord our God he

2. -wake and you shall hear, The Lord our God died
3. shall I come to Thee? When shall my sor - rows
4. from his glor - ious seat The Lord, our God he
5. died up - on the cross; We ne'er shall do for
6. cut down in its flower; We are here to - day and to-
7. stay no long - er here, God bless you all, both

call - èd us, And bid us a - wake and_ pray.

2. on the cross, For us whom he loved so dear.
3. have an end, Thy joy that I may see.
4. bless - èd us With his hea - ven-ly dew so sweet.
5. Je - sus Christ As he has done for us.
6. -mor-row are gone, And we are dead in an hour.
7. great and small, And send you a hap - py New Year.

English traditional

228

174. DOWN IN YON FOREST

Derbyshire tune
(E.R.)

1 Down in yon for-est there stands ____ a hall: ____
2 In ____ that hall ____ there stands ____ a bed: ____
3 At ____ the bed-side there lies ____ a stone: ____
4 Un-der that bed ____ there runs ____ a flood: ____

5 At the bed's foot there grows a thorn:
6 O-ver that bed the moon shines bright:

The bells ____ of Pa-ra-dise I heard ____ them ring:

(1) It's ____ co-ver'd all o-ver with pur-ple and pall:
(2) It's ____ co-ver'd all o-ver with scar-let and red:
(3) Which the sweet Vir-gin Ma — ry knelt ____ up-on:
(4) The ____ one half runs wa-ter, the oth-er runs blood:

5 Which ev-er blows blos — som since he was born:
6 De-no-ting our Sa-viour was born this night:

And I love my Lord Je-sus a-bove a-ny-thing!

Traditional

The references in this Carol are to four interwoven streams of thought – the Passion, the Mass, the Glastonbury Thorn and the Arthurian Legends. Under the figure of a knight dying on a bed, the Saviour's death on the Cross and its representation in the Mass on the altar are here suggested. For a full account see E.C. pp 61 ff.

229

175. A BABE IS BORNE I WYS

F. BAINTON

1. A babe is borne I wys, This world to joy and bliss, His joy shall nev-er fade and miss, And Je-sus is His name, And Je-sus is His name.

2. On Christmas Day at morn,
   This little child was born
   To save us all that were forlorn,
   And Jesus is His name.

3. On Good Friday so soon
   To death He was all done,
   Betwixt the time of morn and noon,
   And Jesus is His name.

4. On Easter Day so swythe
   He rose from death to life
   To make us all both glad and blythe,
   And Jesus is His name.

5. And on Ascension Day
   To heaven He took His way,
   There to abide for aye and aye,
   And Jesus is His name.

N.B. The words are taken from an old MS. in the Westminster Abbey Library, they have been slightly modernized *Wys*—means, know of a certainty.

176. JOY TO THE WORLD

Melody by
NICOLAUS HERMANN, 1485-1561

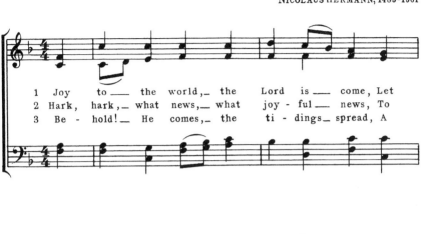

1 Joy to — the world, — the Lord is — come, Let
2 Hark, hark, — what news, — what joy - ful — news, To
3 Be - hold! — He comes, — the ti - dings — spread, A

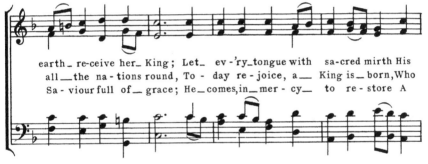

earth — re-ceive her — King; Let — ev-'ry — tongue with sa-cred mirth His
all — the na - tions round, To - day re - joice, a — King is — born, Who
Sa - viour full of — grace; He — comes, in — mer - cy — to re - store A

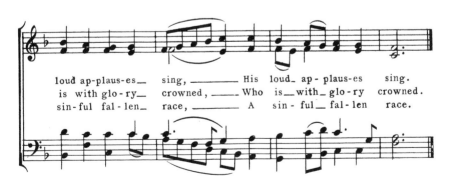

loud ap-plaus-es — sing, ———— His loud — ap - plaus-es sing.
is with glo-ry — crowned, ———— Who is — with — glo-ry crowned.
sin-ful fal - len — race, ———— A sin - ful — fal-len race.

177. THE CEDAR OF LEBANON

Erik Routley

1 The Cedar of Lebanon, Plant of renown,
Hath bowed to the Hyssop his wide spreading crown;
The Son of the Highest an infant is laid
On the breast of the Mother, that lowliest maid.

CHORUS

All_ glo - ry to_ God in the_ high-est we sing,

And_ peace up - on earth through the new - ly_ born King.

2 From the star of the sea the glad sunlight hath shined;
　Sprung Lion of Judah from Naphtali's hind;
　The life from the dying, the rose from the thorn,
　For the maker of all things from maiden is born.
> *CHORUS*

3 The manger of Bethlehem opens once more
　The gates of the Eden where man dwelt of yore,
　And he who is lying, a child in the cave
　Now hath conquered the foeman, hath ransomed the slave.
> *CHORUS*

4 To Him who hath loved us and sent us his Son,
　To Him who the victory for us hath won,
　To Him who sheds on us his sevenfold rays,
　Be all glory and honour, salvation and praise!
> *CHORUS*

> R. F. Littledale

It is here assumed that the cedar is the greatest and the hyssop the least of trees. But the identity of the 'hyssop' (Lev. 14 5-6) is quite uncertain. In v. 2 the Biblical references are to Gen. 49. 9 and 21 (cf. Rev. 5-5).

178. RICHARD DE CASTRE'S PRAYER TO JESUS

Richard Terry

1 Jhe - su, — Lord, that ma-dest me, — And with Thy bles - syd blood — hast bought, — For - give — that — I have grie-véd Thee — With word, and wil, — and — eek — with — thought. —

2 Jhe - su, — for thy woun-dés smerte — On feet and on thyn hand - és - és two, — O make me — meeke and low of herte, — And Thee to love — as — I — schulde do. —

234

Jhe - su, in whom is all my trust,___ That died up -
Jhe - su,___ keepe them that are good,___ A-mende them

on___ the___ rood - é tree,_____ With -
than___ han___ grie - véd Thee,_____ And

- drawe myn___ herte from flesh - li lust,___ And from all
send___ them___ fruites of earth- li food_(cresc.)As each man

world - ly___ van - y - té._____
need - eth___(dim.) in his de - gree._____

Anon. A.D. 1430

235

179. MARY'S DREAM

JOHANNES BRAHMS

1 Saint Ma - ry goes a seek- ing Through Jew - ry, up and down: Through
2 O Look, for she has found him by He - rod's house stood he: By
3 The cross he needs must car - ry through the streets of Je - ru - sa - lem, Through the
4 O see, his brow sur-round-ing, The crown of pierc-ing thorn, The

Jew - ry up and down, un - til God the Lord she found:
He - rod's house stood he, What sor - row for her to see!
streets of Je - ru - sa - lem, To where he will suf-fer shame.
crown of pierc- ing thorn, The cross on shoul-der borne!

O young and old look to it, Ye ne - ver this for - get

That his wounds set wide high Hea - ven's gate!

Old German Carol, translated by H. T. Wade-Gery

180. O LOVE, HOW DEEP, HOW BROAD

O amor, quam ecstaticus

Coutances

ROUEN ANTIPHONER, 1728
(E.R.)

1 O Love, how deep,— how broad,— how high! How pass-ing thought and fan-ta-sy That God, the Son of God,—should take Our mor-tal form— for mor-tals sake.

When this tune is sung in unison throughout, it should be played in a lower key.

2 He sent no Angel to our race
Of higher or of lower place,
But wore the robe of human frame,
And he himself to this world came.

3 For us baptized, for us he bore
His holy fast, and hungered sore;
For us temptations sharp he knew;
For us the tempter overthrew.

4 For us he prayed, for us he taught,
For us his daily works he wrought,
By words and signs and actions, thus
Still seeking not himself but us.

5 For us to wicked men betrayed,
Scourgèd, mocked, in crown of thorns arrayed;
For us he bore the Cross's death;
For us at length gave up his breath.

6 For us he rose from death again,
For us he went on high to reign,
For us he sent his Spirit here
To guide, to strengthen, and to cheer.

7 To him whose boundless love has won
Salvation for us through his Son,
To God the Father glory be
Both now and through eternity.

attributed to St. Thomas à Kempis
tr. B. Webb 1820-85

The Rouen antiphoner prints this tune with the last three notes of line 1 raised by a third (see E.H. 125)

181. CAROL OF THE EXODUS

Old King Cole

English Traditional
(c.w.)

1 Mo - ses, sing un - to Christ, thy King, Who hath won the vic - to -

- ry, And hath laid low haugh-ty Pha - ra - o Un-der-neath the deep Red

Sea. Yea, mer-ry, mer - ry, mer-ry, mer-ry, mer-ry may we be, As

bird up - on the ber - ry of the may or cher - ry tree, While

as we stand with harp in hand On the shore of the Red, Red Sea.

2   God perforce overthrew the horse,
        Rider, car, and axle-tree.
    They sank as lead, and their men lie dead,
        Dead as stone: so mote it be!
    Then merry, merry, etc.

3   His right hand, and His wonder-wand
        Did divide, at His decree,
    The surging wave, and thereby did save
        Us and ours from slavery.
    Then merry, merry, etc.

4   Thou didst blow, and entomb our foe
        In the bottom of the sea:
    And, if dry-shod we went o'er, O God,
        Be ascribed the praise to Thee!
    While merry, merry, etc.

G. R. Woodward

The words were written to provide an Easter carol based on the Exodus story. The connection between the Exodus triumph (Ex. 14-15) and that of Easter is as old as the Scriptures, and is kept in the church's use by the use of Psalm 114 as a special psalm for Easter Day. In this carol the armies of Pharaoh are allegorized as the temptations of the Devil, and the water of the 'Red Sea' (which was probably one of the lakes which now form part of the Suez Canal) symbolizes Death. The action of Moses in (1) being the instrument of God's power over the water and (2) leading the Israelites to the Promised Land are traditionally compared with Christ's conquest of death and his redemption of mankind.

182. LET THE SONG BE BEGUN

Personent Hodie

Melody from Piae Cantiones 1582
(E.R.)

1   Let the song be begun,
    For the battle is done,
    And the victory won:
    And the foe is scatter'd,
    And the prison shatter'd:
    Sing of joy, joy, joy;
    Sing of joy, joy, joy;
    And to-day Raise the lay,
      Gloria in excelsis.

2   They that follow'd in pain
    Shall now follow to reign,
    And the crown shall obtain;
    They were sore assaulted,
    They shall be exalted:
    Sing of rest, rest, rest;
    Sing of rest, rest, rest;
    And again Pour the strain,
      Gloria in excelsis.

3   For the foe nevermore
    Can approach to the shore,
    When the conflict is o'er;
    There is joy supernal;
    There is life eternal;
    Sing of peace, peace, peace;
    Sing of peace, peace, peace;
    Earth and skies Bid it rise,
      Gloria in excelsis.

4   Then be brave, then be true,
    Ye despis'd and ye few,
    For the crown is for you:
    Christ, that went before you,
    Spreads His buckler o'er you:
    Sing of hope, hope, hope;
    Sing of hope, hope, hope;
    And to-day Raise the lay,
      Gloria in excelsis.

J. M. Neale

183. CHRIST IS NOW RISEN AGAIN

Christus ist Erstanden

Medieval melody
(E.R.)

Allegro

1 Christ is now risen again From his death and all his pain; —
2 Had he not risen again We had been lost, this is plain; —
3 Now the time of glad - ness For to sing of his good-ness!

There-fore will we mer - ry be And re - joice with
But since he is risen in - deed Let us love him
There-fore glad now will we be And re - joice in

him glad - ly.
with all speed. } Al - le - lu - ia! Al - le -
him on - ly.

- lu - ia, Al - le - lu - ia, Al - le - lu - ia!

Miles Coverdale, 1488-1569

The ancient melody may be traced as far back as the 12th century.

241

184. FOR JOY OF HEART

Mit Freuden Zart

Melody of the Bohemian Brethren (1566)
(C.W.)

1 For joy of heart come bear a - part And songs of Eas-ter be
Come old and young, at - tune your tongue And set your an-them a -

sing-ing,
- ring-ing. Sal - va-tion's door is e - ver - more By God's own Son wide

o - pen flung; Now of his tri - umphs be tell - ing.

2 Yea, only He full victory
O'er Satan ever hath gained,
And through the strife eternal life
As very God hath attained;
And to His own hath made it known
That, whosoe'er His battle share
To Heaven's gate He will lead them.

3 With joy untold and manifold
Our highest hope He surpriseth;
He'll make His own shine at the sun,
When in his strength he ariseth.
Yea (mark ye this!) to highest bliss,
Make white as snow from sin below,
As angels pure He uplifts them.

4 And so with Thee Thy flock shall be
Made happy once and for ever.
Lord, where Thou art, grant us our part,
And let us fall from Thee never,
But always there Thy praise declare
And sing to Thee eternally,
Where nought again can us sever.

5 Now freely raise your song of praise,
Nor let it ever be ended:
Wide let the fame of Jesus' Name
By word and deed extended
Then shall we be by Him free,
And evermore to Heaven's door
Upon our way befriended.

G. Vetter, 'Mit Freuden zart!'
tr. W. A. Pickard-Cambridge

242

185. SWEET SPRING HAS COME AGAIN TO EARTH

Hilariter

Melody from Cölner Gesangbuch (1623)
(E. R.)

1 Sweet Spring has come a-gain to earth, On Eas-ter Day, on Eas-ter Day, The birds sing out with joy and mirth On Eas-ter Day, on Eas-ter Day.

2 The flowers awake from Winter's gloom,
On Easter Day, on Easter Day,
For Christ has triumphed o'er the tomb
On Easter Day, on Easter Day.

3 Sweet Spring's the time of Hope and Love,
On Easter Day, on Easter Day,
Lift up your hearts to God above,
On Easter Day, on Easter Day.

4 Across the hills a carol rings,
On Easter Day, on Easter Day,
And all the world awakes and sings,
On Easter Day, on Easter Day.

Margaret Rose

243

186. NOW THE GREEN BLADE RISETH

Erik Routley

1 Now the green blade ris - eth from the bur - ied grain,
2 In the grave they laid him, Love whom men had slain,

3 Forth he came at Eas - ter, like the ris - en grain,
4 When our hearts are win - try, griev-ing, or in pain,

Wheat that in dark earth ma - ny days has lain;
Think - ing that ne - ver he would wake a - gain,

He that for three days in the grave had lain,
Thy touch can call us back to life a - gain,

Love lives a - gain, that with the dead has been:
Laid in the earth like grain that sleeps un - seen:

Quick from the dead my ris - en Lord is seen:
Fields of our hearts that dead and bare have been:

CHORUS

Love is come a - gain, Like wheat that spring-eth green.

J. M. C. Crum

187. BEARING MYRRH AND SPICES SWEET

Andantino and very smoothly

Basque Carol (E. P.)

1. Bear - ing myrrh and spi - ces sweet, See the wo - men sad - ly wend - ing In the ear - ly morn - ing grey, Sigh - ings with their fragrance blend - ing___ Sigh - ings with their fra - grance blend - ing.

2. They would seek the lonely tomb.
   Silently with one another,
   For, their heart such love contained,
   Greater than for earthly brother.

3. They had loved Him while He lived,
   Ere the hate of sinners slew Him,
   Now in death, devotion sweet
   Led their willing footsteps to Him.

4. Lo, what wonders meet their gaze,
   And with fear their eyes behold it,
   For the stone was laid aside
   Where angelic hands had rolled it.

5. Lo, an angel now appears
   Clad in robes with snow-white vieing,
   Asking, "Wherefore seek the Lord
   Who is ris'n, where dead were lying."

6. Lord of Life when death appals
   And our night is charged with sorrow,
   Let us see the empty tomb
   With the dawning of the morrow.

   trs. J. Brownlie, *from the Greek*

188. GOOD JOSEPH HAD A GARDEN

GORDON HITCHCOCK

1 Good Jo-seph had a gar-den Close by that sad green hill— Where
2 One eve-ning in that gar-den, Their fa-ces dark with gloom, They

Je-sus died a bit-ter death To save man-kind from ill.—
laid the Sa-viour's bo - dy With-in good Jo - seph's tomb.—

3 There came the ho - ly wo - men With
4 Came Ma - ry to that gar - den And

spi - ces and with tears____ The an - gels tried to
sobbed with heart for - lorn ____ She thought she heard the

com - fort them But could not calm their fears.____
gar - d'ner ask_ "Whom seek - est thou this morn."____

(Solo) 5 She heard her own name spoken,
           And then she lost her care:
           All in his strength and beauty
           The risen Lord stood fair.

(Full) 6 Good Joseph had a garden;
           Amid its trees so tall
           The Lord Christ stood on Easter Day:
           He lives to save us all.

(Full) 7 And as He rose at Easter,
           He is alive for aye,
           The very same Lord Jesus Christ
           Who hears us sing today.

(Unison) 8 Go tell the Lord Christ's message,
             The Easter triumph sing,
             Till all His waiting children know
             That Jesus is their King.

                              A.M. Milner Barry

189. SING SONGS OF JOY TO-DAY

Dutch melody 17th cent
(R.T.)

1 Sing songs of joy to - day Your sweet - est mu - sic
From val - leys far a - way Lift up your voice in

rais - - - - ing,
prais - - - - ing. The Lord is ris'n to -

- day, To Him all praise be giv - en, Lift

up your voice and say _____ That Christ the Lord is

2   Greet Easter Day with joy
     Without a cloud of sadness,
     Let no dark doubts annoy
     For Christ has brought us gladness.

3   No longer Death can hold
     The Christian who believeth,
     His faith is strong and bold
     And Heaven his soul receiveth.

Margaret Rose

190. ALL CREATURES OF OUR GOD AND KING

KÖLN GESANGBUCH, 1623
(E.R.)

1 All crea-tures of our God and King, Al - le - lu - ja,

Lift up your voice and with us sing, Al - le - lu - ja, __

__ Thou burn-ing sun with gold-en beam, Al - le - lu - ja, __

__ Thou sil-ver moon with soft-er gleam: O __ praise __ him,

O __ praise __ him, Al - le - lu - ja, __ Al - le - lu - ja!

Antiphonal treatment is recommended for this carol

2   Thou rushing wind that art so strong,
    Ye clouds that sail in heaven along,
    Thou rising morn, in praise rejoice,
    Ye lights of evening, find a voice:
        O praise him, O praise him,
        Alleluja, alleluja!

3   Thou flowing water pure and clear,
    Make music for thy Lord to hear,
    Thou fire so masterful and bright
    That givest man both warmth and light:

4   Dear mother earth, who day by day
    Unfoldest blessings on our way.
    The flowers and fruits that in thee grow,
    Let them his glory also show:

5   And all ye men of tender heart,
    Forgiving others, take your part,
    Ye who long pain and sorrow bear,
    Praise God and on him cast your care:

6   And thou, most kind ana gentle death,
    Waiting to hush our latest breath,
    Thou leadest home the child of God,
    And Christ our Lord the way hath trod:

7   Let all things their Creator bless,
    And worship him in humbleness,
    Praise, praise the Father, praise the Son,
    And praise the Spirit, three in One:

W. H. Draper
from the Canticle of the Sun,
by St. Francis of Assisi, 1182-1226

Note: The melody of this carol is here given in the version in which it first appeared in 1623.

191. IT IS FINISHED

Edmonton

R. E. PERRIN

1 It is finished! It is finished! as the sun sinks down to rest,
And the sky burns blood and amber in the wonder-weaving West,
Where the clouds make golden islands like the islands of the Blest,
For the day is nearly done.

2 But another day is dawning as the wingèd darkness flies,
And the silver stars keep sentry till another sun shall rise,
For the daylight is eternal, and the sunshine never dies,
It is always marching on.

3 It is finished! It is finished! for the Saviour crucified,
See the soldiers stand in silence where the cruel crowds have cried,
E'en the broken-hearted mother has departed from His side,
For His day is nearly done.

4 But an empty tomb is waiting, and the East is silver grey,
As the angels of the morning trumpet in another day,
See the wounded God go walking down the world's eternal way,
For His task is never done.

5 There's an army thronging round Him as He takes the road tonight,
Can't you see your sons and brothers lined before Him left and right?
Can't you hear their voices calling you to join the host and fight,
For the God who marches on?

G. A. Studdert-Kennedy

252

192. O SONS AND DAUGHTERS

O Filii et Filiae

French Carol
(E.R.)

1 Al - le - lu - ia,— al - le - lu - ia, al-le-lu - ia

O sons and daugh-ters, let_us sing! The King of Heav'n, the glo-rious

King, O'er death to - day rose tri-umph - ing. Al-le-lu - ia!—

2 That Easter morn, at break of day,
The faithful women went their way
To seek the tomb where Jesus lay.
Alleluia!

3 An Angel clad in white they see,
Who sat and spake unto the three,
"Your Lord doth go to Galilee."
Alleluia!

4 That night th' Apostles met in fear;
Amidst them came their Lord most dear,
And said,"My peace be on all here".
Alleluia!

5 When Thomas first the tidings heard,
How they had seen the risen Lord,
He doubted the disciples' word.
Alleluia!

6 "My pierc-ed Side, O Thomas, see;
My Hands, My Feet I show to thee;
Not faithless, but believing be."
Alleluia!

7 No longer Thomas then denied;
He saw the Feet, the Hands, the Side;
"Thou art my Lord and God," he cried.
Alleluia!

8 How blest are they who have not seen,
And yet whose faith hath constant been,
For they eternal life shall win.
Alleluia!

9 On this most holy day of days,
To God your hearts and voices raise
In laud, and jubilee, and praise.
Alleluia!

J. Tisserand, d. 1494
tr. J. M. Neale and others

253

193. YE HUMBLE SOULS THAT SEEK THE LORD

Stewart

HALDANE CAMPBELL STEWART

1 Ye humble souls that seek the Lord
   Chase all your fears away;
And bow with rapture down to see
   The place where Jesus lay.
Thus low the Lord of life was brought,
   Such wonders love can do;
Thus cold in death that body lay,
   That body giv'n to you.

2 Then raise your eyes and tune your songs;
   The Saviour lives again;
Not all the bolts and bars of death
   The Conqueror could retain.
High o'er the angelic bands He rears
   His once dishonoured head;
And through unnumbered years He reigns
   Who dwelt among the dead.

Philip Doddridge, 1702-51 (altd.)

254

194. CHRIST THE LORD IS RISEN TO-DAY

Easter Hymn

Later form (1741) of melody in
Lyra Davidica (1708)

1 Christ the Lord is ris'n to - day }
2 Love's re - deem - ing work is done, }
Al - le - lu - ia!

3 Vain the stone, the watch, the seal; }
4 Lives a - gain our glor-ious King; }
Al - le - lu - ia!

Sons of men and an - gels say; }
Fought the fight, the bat - tle won; }
Al - le - lu - ia!

Christ has burst the gates of hell: }
Where, O Death, is now thy sting? }
Al - le - lu - ia!

Raise your joys and tri - umphs high: }
Lo, our Sun's e - clipse is o'er; }
Al - le - lu - ia!

Death in vain for - bids him rise; }
Once he died our souls to save; }
Al - le - lu - ia!

Sing, ye heav'ns, and earth re - ply. }
Lo, he sets in blood no more. }
Al - le - lu - ia!

Christ has op - ened Pa - ra - dise. }
Where thy vic - to - ry, O grave? }
Al - le - lu - ia!

Charles Wesley, 1707-88

255

195. GOOD CHRISTIAN MEN REJOICE AND SING

Gelobt sei Gott

Melody from M. Vulpius's Gesangbuch (1609)
Harmony by F. Layriz (1853)

Al-le-lu-ia!_____ Al-le-lu-ia!_____ Al-le-lu-ia!

1 Good Christian men, rejoice and sing!
Now is the triumph of our King!
To all the world glad news we bring:
Alleluia!

2 The Lord of life is risen for aye;
Bring flowers of song to strew his way;
Let all mankind rejoice and say
Alleluia!

3 Praise we in songs of victory
That love, that life which cannot die,
And sing with hearts uplifted high
Alleluia!

4 Thy name we bless, O risen Lord,
And sing to-day with one accord
The life laid down, the life restored:
Alleluia!

C. A. Alington

196. THE CALL

ALEXANDER BRENT SMITH

1 Come, my Way, my Truth, — my Life, _____ Such a

2 Come, my Light, my Feast, — my Strength, _____ Such a

3 Come, my Joy, my Love, — my Heart, _____ Such a

Way as gives us breath, Such a Truth as ends all

Light as shows a Feast, Such a Feast as mends in

Joy as none can move, Such a Love as none can

strife, ___ Such a Life _____ as kil - leth Death.

length, ___ Such a Strength _____ as makes his guest.

part, ___ Such a Heart _____ as joys in Love.

George Herbert 1593-1633

When sung by a choir alone, this may effectively be transposed up half a tone.

197. 'TWAS ABOUT THE DEAD OF NIGHT

Scribere Proposui

Piae Cantiones 1582
(E.R.)

1 Twas a - bout the dead of night, And A - thens lay in slum - ber;
Moon-light on the tem-ples slept, And touched the rocks with um - ber.

And the court of Mars were met In grave and rev-'rend num - ber.

Ev - er-more and ev - er-more Chris-tians, sing Al - le - lu - ia!

2 Met they were to hear and judge
The teaching of a stranger;
O'er the ocean he had come,
Through want and toil and danger;
And he worshipp'd for his God
One cradled in a manger.
Evermore and evermore
Christians, sing Alleluia.

3 While he spake against their gods,
And temple vain erection,
Patiently they gave him ear,
And granted him protection;
Till, with bolder voice and mien
He preached the Resurrection.
Evermore and evermore
Christians, sing Alleluia.

4 Some they scoff'd, and some they spake
Of blasphemy and treason;
Some replied with laughter loud
And some replied with reason;
Others put it off until
A more convenient season.
Evermore and evermore
Christians, sing Alleluia.

5 Others heard and scorn'd it then,
Now Europe hath receiv'd it,
Wise men mocked and jeered it once,
Now children have believed it;
This, good Christians, was the day,
That gloriously achieved it.
Evermore and evermore
Christians, sing Alleluia.

J. M. Neale

198. OUR LORD, HIS PASSION ENDED

H. E. DARKE

1 Our Lord, His Passion ended,
  Hath gloriously ascended,
  Yet though from Him divided,
  He leaves us not unguided
    All His benefits to crown
  He hath sent His Spirit down,
  Burning like a flame of fire
  His disciples to inspire.

2 God's Spirit is directing;
  No more they sit expecting;
  But forth to all the nation
  They go with exultation;
    That which God in them hath wrought
  Fills their life and soul and thought;
  So their witness now can do
  Work as great in others too.

3 The centuries go gliding,
  But still we have abiding
  With us that Spirit Holy
  To make us brave and lowly—
    Lowly, for we feel the need:
  God alone is strong indeed;
  Brave, for with the Spirit's aid
  We can venture unafraid.

4 O Lord of every nation
  Fill us with inspiration!
  We know our own unfitness,
  Yet for Thee would bear witness.
    By Thy spirit now we raise
  To the Heavenly Father praise
  Holy Spirit, Father, Son,
  Make us know Thee, ever One.

F. C. Burkitt

259

199. CEREMONIES FOR CHRISTMAS

Old English air

Cheerfully

1. Come bring with a noise, My__ mer-ry, mer-ry boys, The

2. With last year's brand, Light the new block, and For
3. Now drink the strong beer, Cut the white loaf here, The

1. Christ-mas log to the fir - ing, While my good dame she Bids ye

2. good suc - cess in his spend - ing, On your psalt'ries play That
3. while the meat is a - shred-ding, For the rare mince-pie And the

1. all be free, And drink to your heart's de - sir - ing.

2. sweet luck may Come while the__ log is a - teend - ing.
3. plums stand by To fill the__ paste that's a - knead - ing.

Robert Herrick, 1591-1674

200. MERRY CHRISTMAS

Swedish carol

1. Mer-ry Christ-mas, mer-ry Christ-mas, and a hap-py new
2. 'Twas in Beth-le-hem's ci-ty that Je-sus was
3. Oh I wish we could fol-low that star on this

year! Mer-ry Christ-mas, mer-ry Christ-mas, and a hap-py new
born. 'Twas in Beth-le-hem's ci-ty that Je-sus was
day, Oh I wish we could fol-low that star on this

year!__ To__ fa-ther and__ moth-er, and ev-'ry-one
born.__ A__ star it was a-shin-ing both even-ing and
day,__ For__ all the way to hea-ven it light-ens our

Repeat v.1
to finish.

here! To__ fa-ther and mo-ther, and ev-'ry-one here!
morn. A__ star it was a-shin-ing both even-ing and morn.
way. For__ all the way to heav-en it light-ens our way.

Pr. Tom Fletcher

261

201. LET SUCH (SO FANTASTICAL)

English tune (E.R.)

1 Let such (so fan - tas - ti - cal,) lik - ing not this
Nor a - ny-thing ho - nest that an - ci - ent is,

(2nd time)

Give place to the time, that so meet we do see

Ap - poin-ted of God, as it seem - eth to be.

2   At Christmas, good husbands have corn in the ground,
In barn, and in cellar, worth many a pound,
Things plenty in house (beside cattle and sheep),
All sent them (no doubt on) good houses to keep.

3   At Christmas, the hardness of winter doth rage,
A griper of all things, especially age;
Then likely poor people, the young with the old
Be sorest oppressèd with hunger and cold.

4   At Christmas, by labour is little to get;
That wanting, the poorest in danger are set:
What season, then, better of all the whole year,
Thy needy poor neighbour to comfort and cheer?

Thomas Tusser 1524-80

From Tusser's *Hundreth Good Points of Husbandrie* (1557). Tusser's works are the source of many English proverbs, such as 'A pig in a poke', 'The dog in the manger' and 'The stone that is rolling can ga-
ther no moss' – see *Oxford Dictionary of Quotations* p.446. This and the two following carols are
excellent examples (from different regions) of the meeting of sacred and secular which is the essence
of the traditional carol. Their performance needs no reverence, only merriment.

202. GOD BLESS THE MASTER OF THIS HOUSE

Tyrolean melody
(E. R.)

1 God bless the mas-ter of this house, And all that are there-in; And to be-gin this Christ-mas-tide, With mirth now let us sing. *For the Sa-viour of all peo - ple Up - on this time was born,— Who did from death de - li - ver us, When we were left for - lorn.*

2 Then let us all most merry be,
And sing with cheerful voice,
For we have good occasion now
This time for to rejoice.
For the Saviour etc.

3 Then put away contention all,
And fall no more at strife,
Let every man with cheerfulness
Embrace his loving wife.
For the Saviour etc.

4 With plenteous food your houses store,
Provide some wholesome cheer,
And call your friends together
That live both far and near.
For the Saviour etc.

Traditional West Country Carol
from Sandys' Collection, 1833

203. HERE WE COME A-WASSAILING

English Traditional
(E.R.)

1 Here we come a - was - sail-ing a - mong the leaves so green,_____ Here we come a - wand-'ring So fair__ to be seen. *Love and joy come to you, and to you your was-sail too And God bless__ you and send you a hap - py new*

Year,   and God   send you a   hap-py new   year.

2   Our wassail cup is made
      Of the rosemary tree,
      And so is your beer
      Of the best barley.
        Love and joy –

3   We are not daily beggars
      That beg from door to door,
      But we are neighbours' children
      Whom you have seen before.
        Love and joy –

4   Good master and good Mistress,
      As you sit by the fire,
      Pray think of us poor children
      Who are wandering in the mire.
        Love and joy –

5   We have a little purse
      Made of ratching leather skin;
      We want some of your small change
      To line it well within.
        Love and joy –

6   Call up the butler of this house,
      Put on his golden ring:
      Let him bring us a glass of beer,
      And the better we shall sing.
        Love and joy –

7   Bring us out a table,
      And spread it with a cloth;
      Bring us out a mouldy cheese,
      And some of your Christmas loaf
        Love and joy –

8   God bless the master of this house,
      Likewise the mistress too;
      And all the little children
      That round the table go.
        Love and joy –

Traditional

204. IN THOSE TWELVE DAYS

English traditional

In those twelve days let us be glad, In those twelve days let us be glad, For, by his pow'r, God all things made. (1.) What is it that is but one? What is that which is but one? We have but one God a-lone High a-bove all he sits on his throne.

2. What are they which are but two? *(bis)*
Two testaments we're told,
One is the new the other the old.

3. What are they that are but three? *(bis)*
Three persons in Trinity
Father, Son and Holy Ghost.

4. What are they that are but four? *(bis)*
Four Gospels written true
John, Luke, Mark and Matthew.

5. What are they that are but five? *(bis)*
Five senses we have to tell
Grant us thy grace to use them well.

6. What are they that are but six? *(bis)*
Six ages this world shall last,
Five of them are gone and past.

7. What are they that are but seven? *(bis)*
Seven days each week have we,
Six to work and the seventh holy.

8. What are they that are but eight? *(bis)*
Eight beatitudes are giv'n,
Use them well and go to heaven.

9. What are they that are but nine? *(bis)*
Nine degrees of angels high,
Which praise God continually.

10. What are they that are but ten? *(bis)*
Ten commandments God hath given
Keep them right and go to heaven.

11. What are they that are but eleven? *(bis)*
Eleven thousand virgins did partake
And Suffer'd death for Jesu's sake.

12. What are they that are but twelve? *(bis)*
Twelve Apostles Christ did choose
To preach the Gospel to the Jews.

English traditional

266

205. WELCOME YULE

SYDNEY H. NICHOLSON

Wel-come Yule, thou mer-ry man In wor-ship of this ho-ly day.

Wel-come Yule, Wel - come Yule!

1 Wel-come be thou hea - ven King,
2 Wel-come be ye Ste-phen and John,
3 Wel-come be ye good New Year,
4 Wel-come be ye Can - dle-mas,
5 Wel-come be ye that are here,

1 Wel-come born_ in one morn-ing, Wel-come for_ whom we shall sing:
2 Wel-come In-no-cents ev-'ry one, Wel-come Thomas Mar - tyr one:
3 Wel-come Twelfth day, both in fere, Wel-come Saintes lief_ and dear:
4 Wel-come be_ ye Queen of bliss, Wel-come both to more_ and less:
5 Wel-come all_ and make good cheer, Wel-come all a - no - ther year:

vv 1-4   *last verse*

Wel-come Yule,_ Wel - come Yule! Wel - come Yule!

Traditional

267

206. THE TWELVE DAYS OF CHRISTMAS

English traditional
(G.H.)

Unison

Verse 1

The first day of Christ-mas my true-love sent to me, A

Verses 2, 3 and 4

Par-tridge in a pear tree. The { second / third / fourth } day of Christ-mas my

Verses 3 and 4, repeat for V.4

true-love sent to me

four col-ly birds,
three french hens,

two tur-tle doves and a par-tridge in a pear tree.

Note. This is a traditional English singing game but the melody of five gold rings was added by Richard Austin whose fine setting (Novello) should be consulted for a fuller accompaniment.

207. CANDLEMAS EVE CAROL

Basque Melody
(E. P.)

Spirited

1. Down with the rose-ma - ry___ and bays, Down with the mis-tle - toe;___ In-
2. The hol - ly hith - er - to___ did sway: Let box now dom-in - eer.___ Un-

- stead of hol - ly, now up-raise The green - er box, for show._
- til the danc - ing Eas - ter day, Or Eas-ter's eve ap - pear.

Thus times and sea-sons oft___ do shift; Each thing his turn doth hold;___ New

thoughts and things now do suc - ceed, As form - er things grow old.___

3.
Then youthful box, which now hath grace,
Your houses to renew,
Grown old, surrender must his place
Unto the crispèd yew.
   Thus times *etc.*

4.
When yew is out, then birch comes in,
And many flowers beside,
Both of a fresh and fragrant kin,
To honour Whitsuntide.
   Thus times *etc.*

5.
Green rushes then, and sweetest bents,
With cooler oaken boughs,
Come in for comely ornaments,
To readorn the house.
   Thus times *etc.*

Robert Herrick (1591-1674)
Chorus adapted G.H.

270

208. THE CHERRY TREE CAROL
Part I

English Traditional
(R.T.)

1 Jo - seph____ was an old____ man, And an
2 Jo - seph and Ma - ry walk - èd Through an
3 0____ then be - spoke____ Ma - ry, With____

4 Go____ to the tree, ____ Ma - ry, And it
5 Go____ to the tree, ____ Ma - ry, And it
6 Then____ bow - èd down the high - est tree Un -
7 0____ eat your cher - ries Ma - ry, 0____

1 old ___ man___ was___ he, _____ When ___ he wed - ded ___
2 or - chard___ so___ good, _____ There was cher - ries and___
3 words___ meek ___ and___ kind, _____ 'Pluck___ me one cher-ry

4 shall___ bow___ to___ thee, _____ And the high - est branch of
5 shall___ bow___ to___ thee, _____ And___ you shall ga - ther
6 - to___ Ma - ry's___ hand; _____ Then___ she cried, 'See ___
7 eat your cher - ries___ now, _____ 0___ eat your cher-ries,

1 Ma - ry In the land of Ga - li - lee.
2 ber - ries So____ red as a - ny blood.
3 Jo - seph, For____ they run in my mind?

4 all _____ Shall bow down to Ma - ry's knee.
5 cher - ries By____ one, and two and three.
6 Jo - seph, I have cher - ries at com - mand?
7 Ma - ry, That____ grow up - on the bough.

*The first note of the melody (in brackets) is not in the original; it is inserted to meet the exigencies of the verses.

271

K

THE CHERRY TREE CAROL
Part II

English Traditional
(R.T.)

8 As Joseph was a-walking He heard an angel sing: This night shall be born Our heavenly King. He neither shall in housen Be born, nor yet in hall, Nor bed, nor downy pillow, But in an oxes stall.

9 He neither shall be clothèd
   In purple nor in pall,
   But in the fair white linen
   That usen babies all.
   He neither shall be rockèd
   In silver nor in gold,
   But in a wooden cradle
   That rocketh on the mould

10 He neither shall be christen'd
    In white wine nor in red,
    But with the fair spring water
    As we were christenèd.
    As Joseph was a-walking
    He heard an angel sing;
    This night shall be born
    Your heaven-ly King.

For a modern tune by Terry to these words see 10.

THE CHERRY TREE CAROL
Part III

English Traditional Carol
(R.T.)

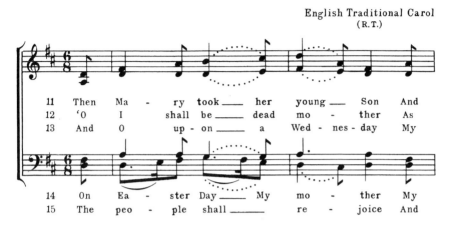

11 Then Ma - ry took —— her young —— Son And
12 'O I shall be —— dead mo - ther As
13 And O up - on —— a Wed - nes - day My

14 On Ea - ster Day —— My mo - ther My
15 The peo - ple shall —— re - joice And

set Him on her knee: —— 'I — pray Thee now — my
the stones in the wall; —— O the stones — in — the
vow I will — make, —— And up - on —— Good — Fri -

ris - ing will —— be, —— O the sun —— and — the
the birds they shall sing —— To — see —— the — up -

dear - est Child Tell how — this world shall be? ——
streets, mo - ther, Shall sor - row for — Me all. ——
day —— My death —— I — will take. ——

moon, mo - ther, They shall up - rise — with Me. ——
- ris - ing Of the — hea - ven - ly King. ——

273

209. THE HOLY WELL

Traditional
Arr. T.W.

1 As it fell out one May morn - ing, And up -
'To play, to play, sweet Je - sus shall go, And to

- on a bright ho-li - day, Sweet Je-sus asked of his dear Mo - ther If
play now get you gone; And let me hear of no com-plaint At

he might go to play If he might go to play.
night when you come home, At night when you come home.'

2   Sweet Jesus went down to yonder town,
        As far as the Holy Well,
    And there did see as fine children
        As any tongue can tell.
    He said, 'God bless you every one,
        And your bodies Christ save and see!
    And now, little children, I'll play with you,
        And you shall play with me.'

Tune collected by Cecil Sharp, at Camborne in 1913.   The words are collated from both
Sandys and Sidgwick and vary slightly from those given in the Folk Song Journal Vol. V, page
4, where the tune is printed.

3   But they made answer to him, 'No!
       Thou art meaner than us all;
    Thou art but a simple fair maid's child,
       Born in an ox's stall'.
    Sweet Jesus turned him round about,
       Neither laughed, nor smiled, nor spoke;
    But the tears came trickling from his eyes
       Like waters from the rock.

4   Sweet Jesus turned him round about,
       To his mother's dear home went he,
    And said,'I have been in yonder town,
       As after you may see:
    I have been down in yonder town,
       As far as the Holy Well;
    There did I meet with as fine children
       As any tongue can tell.

5   'I said,"God bless you every one,
       And your bodies Christ save and see!
    And now, little children, I'll play with you,
       And you shall play with me".'
    But they made answer to me "No";
       They were lords' and ladies' sons,
    And I the meanest of them all,
       Born in an ox's stall'.

6   'Though you are but a maiden's child,
       Born in an ox's stall,
    Thou art the Christ, the King of Heaven,
       And the Saviour of them all!
    Sweet Jesus, go down to yonder town,
       As far as the Holy Well,
    And take away those sinful souls,
       And dip them deep in hell'.

7   'Nay, nay,' sweet Jesus smiled and said;
       'Nay, nay, that may not be,
    For there are too many sinful souls
       Crying out for the help of me'.
    Then up spoke the angel Gabriel,
       Upon a good set steven
    'Although you are but a maiden's child,
       You are the King of Heaven!'

Traditional

This may be sung with equal appropriateness to the tune of No. 42

210. THERE WAS A MAID

Dutch Carol of the 15th century
(R.T.)

1 There was a maid so love-ly,___ Al-though she was so
2 Said she: No won-der is it ___ That so my col-our

3 Then made He as to leave her___ And hid Hid face a-
4 Her lov-er, all com-pas-sion ___ Came back to her a-

poor;___ The King of Kings would make her His
flies,___ That faint I grow and pal-er With

-way,___ And so she bid-ed lone-ly A
-gain ___ And show'd how love had thriv-en On

own for ev-er-more. Said He: My rose so red, To
ev-'ry day that dies, It weak-ens hope with-in, My

sea-son and a day. She said: Now poor in-deed And
hope that wells from pain. The Cross must needs be nigh To

dim. e rall. *a tempo* *rit.*

li-ven thee I bled,___ Why is thy col-our fled?
pov-er-ty and sin ___ Too great such love to win.

bound-less is my need ___ With none my suit to speed.
love that aims so high ___ Till sor-row turn to joy.

tr. J. O'Connor

276

211. I SAW THREE SHIPS

Words and tune traditional

English traditional melody
Descant by C.S. Lang

2. Choir.   And what was in those ships all three?
3. Congr.   Our Saviour Christ and his lady.
4. Choir.   Pray, whither sailed those ships all three?
5. Congr.   O, they sailed into Bethlehem.
6. Descant. And all the bells on earth shall ring,
7. Choir.   And all the angels in Heaven shall sing,
8. Congr.   And all the souls on earth shall sing.
9. Descant. Then let us all rejoice amain!

212. THE SEVEN JOYS

Traditional
(R.T.)

The first good joy that Ma - ry had, It was the joy of
one; ___ To see the bles - sed Je - sus Christ When
He was first her Son. ___

CHORUS

When He was first her
Son, good Man; And bles - sed may He be. ___ Both

278

Fa-ther, Son and Ho-ly Ghost, To all e-ter-ni-ty.____

2   The next good joy that Mary had
    It was the joy of two,
    To see her own son Jesus Christ
    Making the lame to go.

3   The next good joy that Mary had
    It was the joy of three,
    To see her own son Jesus Christ
    Making the blind to see.

4   The next good joy that Mary had
    It was the joy of four,
    To see her own son Jesus Christ
    Reading the Bible o'er.

5   The next good joy that Mary had
    It was the joy of five,
    To see her own son Jesus Christ
    Raising the dead to life.

6   The next good joy that Mary had
    It was the joy of six,
    To see her own son Jesus Christ
    Rise from the crucifix.

7   The next good joy that Mary had
    It was the joy of seven,
    To see her own son Jesus Christ
    Ascending into heaven.

                            Traditional

279

213. THE TRUMPET CAROL

Burgundian
(R.T.)

1 Tan-ta.-ra! Migh-ty God! Let me shat-ter the si - lence,

Were it the ve-ry last breath I gave Thee of__ life!__

My pu - ny__ pow-ers, na - tive, To flou-rish on the fife,

Thee on__ the__ stir - ring__ trum-pet Pro - claim.

2   Given this holy day's universal devotion,
       Clarions utter praise, as Thy glories demand,
       Grant every land, all ocean
          To quiver to the peal,
       Sharing the blithe emotion
          I feel.

3   Right on the stroke of time camest Thou to the rescue,
       Rescuing what the fiend had contended to mar:
       Thy Mother cast in stable,
          Thy poverty, Thy star,
       Foil the Abominable
          From far.

4   Chaldean vigilance had its spy-glasses mounted,
       Quick to discern in East how the star was increased,
       Rightly surmising early
          Why such a light should spring ;
       'Lo! He is here, Messiah
          The King'

5   Thence to Judea come, gave they no peace to any,
       Saying:'Where is He born, your young King of the Jews?'
       Herod, the news o'erhearing,
          In fury froze to ice,
       Calling High Councils, craving
          Advice.

6   Meanwhile for better aim to destroy Hope of nations
       Feigning to fear Thy name, and the Magi he sent:
       I,too would offer worship,
          So bring me word therefrom
       Herod the King, Tarara
          Pom Pom!

7   O Jesu Christ our cure has cost Thee many phials,
       The heavy trials bought us a royal release,
       Thy woes eternal comfort.
          Our Christmas shall not cease,
       Evermore warbling carols
          Of peace.

Burgundian Noel, tr. J. O'Connor

(1) The mordants should not be attempted by the singers, but may be played by the accompanist.

214. THE GOSSOON AND THE GAFFER CAROL

Dieu vous gard', noste mèstre

Provençal
(R.T.)

GOSSOON

1 God save you kind - ly gaf - fer, Will you get an - o - ther lad? Don't think I want to chaf - fer, For the wa - ges is - n't bad.

GAFFER

Now you can't go off so— fly!— You young fel - lows, (Win - dy

282

bel-lows.) Think you can't have e-nough li - ber - ty.

GOSSOON 2 I'm going on a journey
    To the town of Bethlehem
    I want my bit o' money
    For to pay my way with them.

GAFFER If you go before you're clear
    Law engages
    You no wages
    Until the end of another year.

GOSSOON 3 Now take my word my master
    And come you away with I,
    You'll see there's no disaster
    In adoring the God most high.

GAFFER Do you want to pull my leg?
    Taradiddles!
    Sticks o' fiddles!
    I'm not the son of a larnèd pig!

GOSSOON 4 But here's my mates already,
    And they give their solemn word
    The moon is up and steady
    And they're off to see the Lord.

GAFFER Then I may as well go too.
    This cold weather
    Step together.
    Keep to the fields, they're as green as you.

Provençal Noël
tr. J. O'Connor

283

215. GOOD KING WENCESLAS

A Spring Song of the 13th Century
(Tempus adest floridum)
Melody from *Piae Cantiones,* 1582
(R. T.)

1 Good King Wen-ces - las look'd out, On the feast of Steph - en;
2 "Hith - er, page, and stand by me, If thou know'st it, tell - ing,

When the snow lay round a - bout_ Deep, and crisp, and e - ven;
Yon - der pea - sant, who is he?_ Where and what his dwell - ing?"

Bright-ly shone the moon that night, Though the frost was cru - el,
"Sire, he lives a good league hence, Un - der-neath the moun-tain;

When a poor man came in_ sight, Gath-'ring win-ter fu - el.
Right a-gainst the fo - rest fence, By Saint Ag-nes' foun - tain."

3   "Bring me flesh and bring me wine,
        Bring me pine-logs hither;
    Thou and I will see him dine,
        When we bear them thither."
    Page and Monarch forth they went,
        Forth they went together,
    Through the rude wind's wild lament,
        And the bitter weather.

4   "Sire, the night is darker now,
        And the wind blows stronger,
    Fails my heart, I know not how;
        I can go no longer."
    "Mark my footsteps, good my page;
        Tread thou in them boldly;
    Thou shalt find the winter's rage
        Freeze thy blood less coldly."

5   In his master's steps he trod,
        Where the snow lay dinted;
    Heat was in the very sod
        Which the Saint had printed.
    Therefore, Christian men, be sure,
        Wealth or rank possessing,
    Ye who now will bless the poor,
        Shall yourselves find blessing.

                      J. M. Neale

216. OUR MASTER HATH A GARDEN

Heer Jesus heeft een hofken

Dutch carol melody (17th century)
(R.T.)

1 Our Mas-ter hath a gar-den which fair flow'rs a-

-dorn. There will I go and ga-ther both at eve and

CHORUS

morn; There an-gel choirs tune ju-bi-lant lyres,—With

dul-ci-mer, lute and trum - pet— proud, and cla-rion loud and

gen - tle sooth - ing flute. With trum - pet___ proud, and

cla - rion loud, and gen - tle sooth - ing flute.

2 The lily white that bloometh there is Purity,
   The fragrant violet is surnamed Humility;
     There angel choirs, etc.

3 The lovely damask rose is there called Patience,
   The rich and cheerful marigold Obedience,
     There angel choirs, etc.

4 One plant is there with crown bedight, the rest above,
   With crown imperial, and this plant is Holy Love;
     There angel choirs, etc.

5 But still of all the flow'rs the fairest and the best,
   Is Jesus Christ, the Lord Himself, His name be blest,
     There angel choirs, etc.

6 O Jesu, my chief good and sole felicity,
   Thy little garden make my ready heart to be.
     There angel choirs, etc.

J. M. Neale
(altered)

217. DING DONG! MERRILY ON HIGH

Tune, *Branle de l'Official*
from Thoinot Arbeau's *Orchésographie,* 1588
(C.W.)

1. Ding dong! mer-ri-ly on high in heav'n the bells are ring - ing:

2. E'en so here be-low, be - low, let stee - ple bells be swung-en,
3. Pray you, du-ti-ful-ly prime your Mat - in chime, ye ring - ers;

1. Ding dong! ve-ri-ly the sky is riv'n with An-gel sing - ing.

2. And *i - o, i - o, i - o,* by priest and peo-ple sung-en.
3. May you beau-ti-ful-ly rime your Eve - time Song, ye sing - ers:

Glo . . . .

. . . *ri-a, Ho - san-na in ex - cel - sis!*

G. R. Woodward

288

INDEXES

INDEX OF FIRST LINES AND TITLES

(Where a title differs from the first words of a carol, it is printed separately in *italics*.)

293

INDEX OF COMPOSERS

INDEX OF AUTHORS AND TRANSLATORS

(Numbers in brackets refer to translations.)

INDEX OF SUBJECTS

297

INDEX OF NATIONAL AND CULTURAL ORIGINS

ENGLISH TRADITIONAL

Many of these carols and tunes were collected in Cornwall by Davies Gilbert and William Sandys at the beginning of the 19th century. Others were collected by such folk-song authorities as Cecil Sharp, R. Vaughan Williams and Lucy Broadwood in other parts of the country. The exact origin of any carol or tune is bound to be unascertainable. Where no place of origin is here given, the carol or tune may be presumed to come from the West Country, so far as we know.

Words and Music:	1, 9 (Devon), 17, 18 (London tune), 19, 21 (Kent), 22 (Sussex), 23, 24 (Dorset), 25, 26, 27, 28 (Surrey), 29 (words, London, 1642; tune probably London), 35 (18th century), 165, 166 (Gloucester tune), 167, 168, 169, 170 (18th century words), 171 (Sussex), 172, 173, 174 (Derbyshire version), 203 (London), 204, 206 (Northumberland)?, 208, 209, 211 (Northumberland), 212.
Words:	10, 164, 202.
Music:	3 (Nursery-rhyme), 15 (Surrey), 30, 31, 32, 33 (London), 34 (London), 49 (Nursery-rhyme), 50 (Sussex), 51 (Wilts.), 58 (Devon), 181, 199, 201.
IRISH	words and music: 8; music: 92
WELSH	music: 93.
SCOTTISH	words and music: 90, 91; words: 89.
CANADIAN	words and music: 94, 95.
U.S.A.	words and music: 96, 98, 99; words: 15, 157.
AUSTRALIAN	words and music: 100–1.

ENGLISH MANUSCRIPTS

15*th cent.*	words and music: 20, 71, 72, 73, 74, 75; words: 53, 79, 122, 174, 175, 178.
16*th cent.*	words and music: 69, 70, 76.
18*th cent.*	music: 36, 38 (Leicester), 39 (West Country), 40 (Dorset), 41 (Dorset).
ENGLISH HYMNS	155, 156, 159, 160, 193, 194, 195.
from Latin originals:	12, 13, 158, 180, 192.
from German originals:	16, 161, 162, 163.

FRENCH

Traditional Noels:	words (original) and music: 102 (Flemish), 103–116, 213, 214.
Manuscripts (ancient):	192, 217.
Music:	Hymn tunes (18th cent.), 47, 180; Traditional: 60, ·117; Manuscript: 55.

BASQUE and SPANISH

Catalan:	118.
Basque (music only):	5, 119–126, 187, 207.

FROM A BROADSIDE PUBLISHED ABOUT 1800

Printed in Great Britain by Hobbs the Printers of Southampton 10/87